SOMEHOW, HE **KNOWS** HE'S ONLY DREAMING.

THESE ANCIENT STREETS -- THE GROTESQUE GARGOYLES -- THEY COULD NEVER EXIST IN THE MEGA-CITY. SINISTER MONKS WITH BIG KNIVES...? GET **REAL**, CHIC! THIS IS **2115!**

BUT HE RUNS ANYWAY, AND THEIR FOOTSTEPS ECHO LIKE COFFIN LIDS BEHIND HIM.

A NIGHTMARE, THAT'S ALL IT IS. HE'LL WAKE UP SOON... WON'T HE?

HE'S STRANGELY SURPRISED TO HEAR THE HARSH RASP OF HIS OWN BREATHING. IT SEEMS *TOO* REAL -- TOO *INTENSE* -- TO BE JUST A DREAM.

A CHILL FEELING OF DREAD SPREADS OUTWARD FROM HIS GUT. HE BREAKS INTO A RUN --

BUT THERE'S NOWHERE TO GO.

DOCTOR CHIC PURDIE FEELS COLD SWEAT DRIP DOWN HIS FACE. DESPERATELY, HE TRIES TO WILL HIMSELF AWAKE --

AWAKE! AWAKE!

BUT AS SURE AS HE KNOWS HE'S DREAMING, HE KNOWS THAT HIS TIME HAS COME --

--NO HISTORY OF HEART TROUBLE, JUDGE. HE JUST WAKENED UP SCREAMING--THEN HE DIED!

MASSIVE CORONARY ALL RIGHT, DREDD! LIKE HIS HEART **EXPLODED!**

HMM. EXACTLY THE SAME AS THE **OTHER** MEGA-CHEM SCIENTIST WHO DIED THIS WEEK!

I SMELL A LARGE RAT!

KARYN-- SEE WHAT YOUR **PSI** POWERS TURN UP!

CHEEZ! SOME NIGHTMARE...!

NOTHING TO SHOW IT WASN'T NATURAL. ONLY... WELL, THE RESIDUAL IMAGES ARE STRONGER THAN I'D EXPECT. **MUCH** STRONGER.

I'D RECOMMEND A FULL **BLOOD ANALYSIS!**

ARRANGE IT. KEEP ME POSTED!

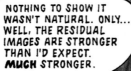

I'LL BE AT **MEGA-CHEM!**

DOC PURDIE? BUT -- THAT'S **FOUR** OF MY TOP TEAM DEAD NOW!

MECACHEM

HOME OF THE WORLD'S FAVORITE CHEMICAL'S

DO YOU THINK SOMEONE COULD BE TRYING TO **SABOTAGE** US?

YOU TELL ME. WHY WOULD ANYBODY **WANT** TO...?

MONEY, I SUPPOSE. WE'RE WORKING ON A NEW MALTED SOY **BEDTIME DRINK**, WITH A BUILT-IN "FEELGOOD" FACTOR. THE MARKET'S WORTH **BILLIONS**.

ANY ONE OF OUR COMPETITORS MIGHT BE WILLING TO **KILL** TO **STOP** US!

COULD BE. BUT I'D LIKE TO CHECK THE **HOME-GROWN** SUSPECTS FIRST.

DID YOU KILL DOCTOR CHIC PURDIE?

NO!

TRUE.

DID YOU KILL DOCTOR HEATHEN BARNARD?

NO!

DID YOU KILL DOCTOR BENNY CASEY?

NO!

DREDD.? KARYN. I GOT THE ANALYSIS ON PURDIE. THE LEVELS OF ACHETYLTHOLINE IN HIS BLOODSTREAM WENT OFF THE SCALE!

LEVELS OF **WHAT**?

ACHETYLTHOLINE. IT'S THE CHEMICAL THAT MAKES US **DREAM**. PURDIE HAD SO MUCH OF IT, IT **HAD** TO BE EXTERNALLY INTRODUCED!

IT WOULD HAVE GIVEN HIM **NIGHTMARES** HE **COULDN'T** WAKE UP FROM -- PUTTING HIS **HEART** UNDER INCREDIBLE **STRESS**!

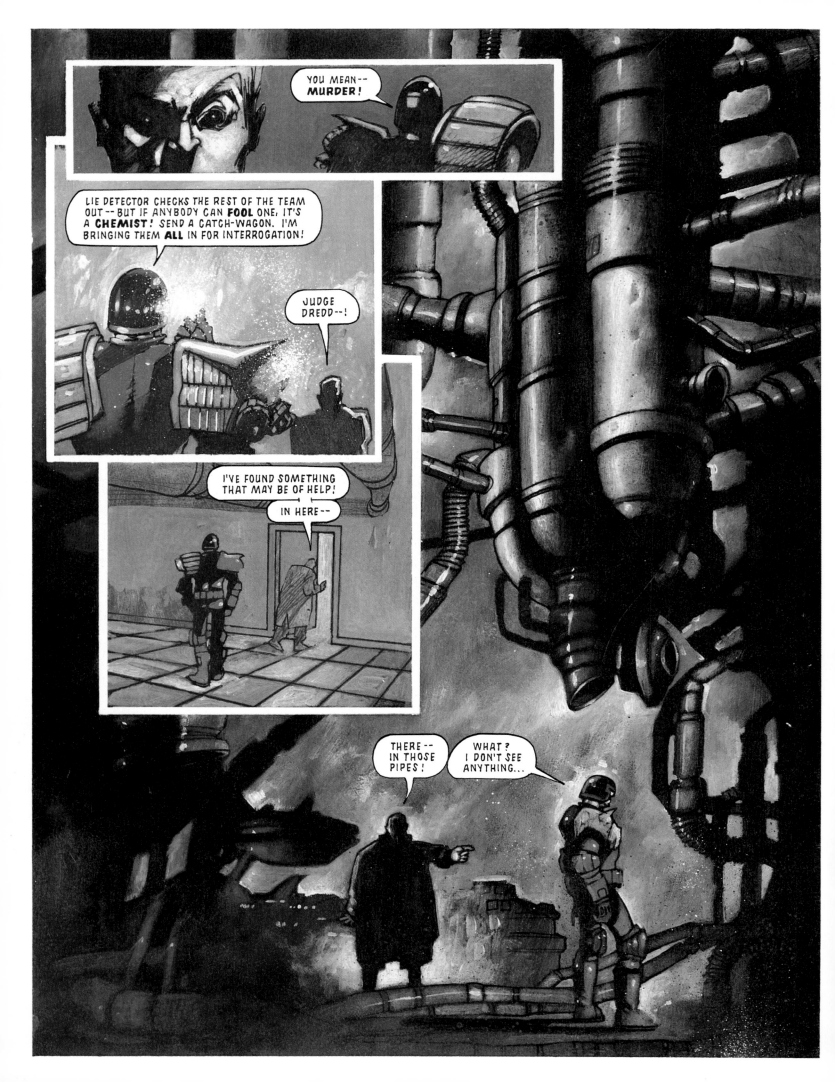

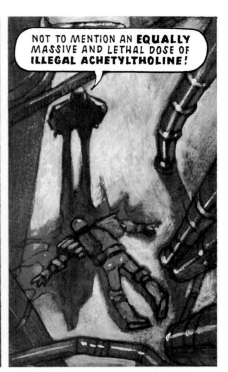

PROFESSOR YOONG! WHAT ARE YOU DOING?

WHAT DOES IT **LOOK** LIKE, FOSTER? I'M **STEALING** THE SOY-MALT **DATA-BASE!**

BUT--THAT HAS ALL OUR **RESEARCH** ON IT! WITHOUT IT THE ENTIRE PROGRAMME WILL GRIND TO A **HALT!**

YOU'RE VERY ASTUTE, FOSTER. YOU SHOULD APPLY FOR A **PROMOTION**--

-- WHEN YOU COME ROUND!

WUNKK

EXIT

CHEM-IZ- MEGA CHEM

DAMN!

CATCH

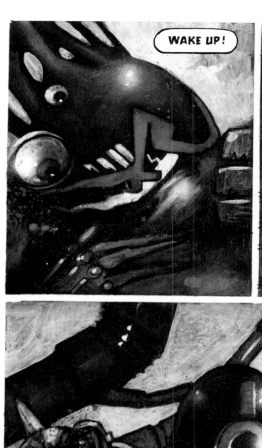

This feature profiles all of Judge Dredd's annuals and yearbooks since 1980, with a complete index, background and 12 things you never knew about these volumes!

The Story So Far...

This year's Judge Dredd Yearbook is the 14th edition in an annual series of mighty tomes featuring Mega-City One's toughest lawman, his foes and fellow judges!

Judge Dredd got his first annual (cover-dated 1981) in 1980, just three years after his debut in the pages of 2000 AD. He had rapidly become the leading character in the weekly comic and became the first character from the title to receive his own annual. (The only character created by 2000 AD to get an annual since is Rogue Trooper, in 1990.)

The decision to give Dredd his own annual was a daring one - rarely did a single story have enough depth to sustain a 96-page volume.

But writer John Wagner (assisted by a few others) had developed the world of Dredd, giving the future lawman a complete environment and history.

The company that then published 2000 AD, IPC, had a 'five-year reprint' rule. This stated stories from its titles could not be reprinted within five years of their first publication.

This meant no Dredd stories from 2000 AD were available to be reprinted in the annuals until the 1982 cover-dated volume. (A similar problem faced the 2000 AD annuals, which were forced to reprint material from other, often wildly incongruous sources.)

But rather than filling out the Dredd annual with unrelated material, the editors wisely used the opportunity to provide a lot of background features about Dredd's world.

Even the staples ideas of annuals such as quiz pages were adapted to reflect elements of the host character, with a You Are a Judge Quiz.

The first Dredd annual established a format that was to remain unchanged for 11 years. The book opened with a contents pages and a six-page colour story. Then there were 32 pages of black and white strips and features, 16 pages of colour strip in the centre section, another 32 pages of black and white material and a final seven-page colour story.

The first Dredd annual was a success and another volume has followed every year since. The format changed with the 1992 cover-dated book, which was renamed the Judge Dredd Yearbook.

After 11 hardback years, the annual became a soft-cover yearbook with a double-gatefold wrap-around cover. The yearbook actually gained four pages inside because the annuals counted the covers as part of their pages.

The revamped yearbooks have proved to be another success with this year's volume in your hands the third in this format.

I HOPE YOU'RE RIGHT.

JUDGE DREDD ANNUALS
AND YEARBOOKS INDEX

JUDGE DREDD ANNUAL
1981   £1.80

COVER ART: Judge Dredd by Brian Bolland

COLOUR STRIPS:

Judge Dredd in "Pinboing Wizard" (6 pg)
Script: John Wagner Art: Mike McMahon

Judge Dredd in "Compulsory Purchase!"
(7 pg) Script: John Wagner Art: Mike
McMahon

Judge Dredd in "The Fear that made
Milwaukee Famous" (16 pg) Script: John
Wagner Art: Mike McMahon

BLACK & WHITE STRIPS:

Judge Dredd in "The First Judge Dredd"
(5 pg) Script: John Wagner Art: Carlos
Ezquerra

"Max Normal, The Pinstripe Freak!" (11 pg)
Script: Alan Grant Art: Casanovas

"Walter the Wobot, Friend of Dwedd"
(8 pg) Script: G. P. Rice Art: Brendan
McCarthy

"Shok!" (Walter's Robo-Tale) (7 pg)
Script: Steve MacManus/Kevin O'Neill
Art: Kevin O'Neill

TEXT STORY:
"Mad Tooth's Run" (6 pg) Story: Jack Adrian
Illustrations: Dave Gibbons

FEATURES:
The Judge Dredd Story; Judge Dredd's
Lawgiver; The Cursed Earth Journey; You Are
a Judge Quiz; Judge Dredd's Lawmaster; The
Changing Face of Dredd; Trans-Time Holidays
invite You to Mega-City One; Walter's Works.

JUDGE DREDD ANNUAL
1982   £1.95

COVER: Judge Dredd by Mike McMahon

COLOUR STRIPS:
Judge Dredd in "Anatomy of a Crime"
(6 pg) Script: John Wagner Art: Mike
McMahon

Judge Dredd in "The Vampire Effect" (16 pg)
Script: John Wagner Art: Mike McMahon

Judge Dredd in "Mega-City Rumble"
(7 pg) Script: John Wagner Art: Mike
McMahon

BLACK & WHITE STRIPS:

"The Mean Machine Goes To Town!"
(6 pg) Script: Alan Grant Art: Robin Smith

Walter the Wobot in "Woad to Wuin"
(6 pg) Script: G. Rice Art: S. Kyte

Judge Dredd in "Judge Whitey" (reprint from
2000 AD Prog 2) Script: John Wagner
Art: Mike McMahon (5 pg)

Max Normal, the Pinstripe Freak   (untitled)
(6 pg) Script: Kelvin Gosnell Art: Jose
Casanovas

Judge Dredd in "The Brother of Darkness"
(reprint from Prog 4) Script: M. Shaw Art:
Mike McMahon (4 pg)

TEXT STORY:
"Desperadoes of the Cursed Earth"
(7 pg) Story: Jack Adrian Illustrations: Dave
Gibbons

FEATURES:
Data Files on Otto Sump, Judge Hershey, Max
Normal; The Judge Dredd Interview; Are You
a MegaMind Quiz; Angel Gang family photo
album; Je Suis La Loi!; The Mega-Times; The
Judge Child Journey; Easy Riders; Hall of
Infamy; Lawmaster Road Test; Ode to Dredd.

JUDGE DREDD ANNUAL
1983   £2.75

COVER: Judge Dredd by Brian Bolland

COLOUR STRIPS:
Judge Dredd in "The Big Itch" (6 pg) Script:
John Wagner Art: Carlos Ezquerra

Judge Dredd in "Behold The Beast"
(16 pg) Script: John Wagner Art: Carlos
Ezquerra

Judge Dredd in "It's Happening on Line 9" (7
pg) Script: John Wagner Art: Carlos Ezquerra

BLACK & WHITE STRIPS:
Max Normal, the Pinstripe Freak   (untitled)
(6 pg) Script: Alan Grant Art: Jose
Casanovas

Judge Dredd in "The Comic Pusher" (reprint
from Prog 20) Script: John Wagner Art:
Mike McMahon (4 pg)

"The Mean Machine Gets Married!"
(6 pg) Script: Alan Grant Art: Robin Smith

Judge Dredd in "Komputel" (reprint from
Prog 32) Script: R. Flynn Art: Mike McMahon
(5 pg)

TEXT STORY:
"A Day in the Death of Citizen Egg"
(8 pg) Story: Alan Grant Illustrations: Dave
Gibbons

"I Was a Teenage Perp!"   (7 pg) Story:
Alan Grant Illustrations: Brett Ewins

POOR FOOL... IF ONLY HE'D OBEYED THE *LAW!* DO WHAT YOU CAN FOR HIM, DOCTOR. *SPARE NO EXPENSE.*

Ewins/Steve Dillon

FEATURES:
Who was That Masked Perp?;
Drokkbusters!; Dredd Covers; Dredd
Dictionary of Quotations.

JUDGE DREDD ANNUAL
1988   £3.50

COVER: Judge Dredd by John Higgins

COLOUR STRIPS:
Judge Dredd in "Last of the Bad Guys"
(29 pg) Script: John Wagner & Alan Grant
Art: John Higgins

BLACK & WHITE STRIPS:
Anderson, Psi Division (untitled)   (8 pg)
Script: Alan Grant Art: Mike Collins

Judge Dredd in "The DNA Man" (reprint
from Prog 113-115) Script: John Wagner
Art: Brett Ewins (16 pg)

Judge Dredd - Daily Star strip reprints
(12 pg) Script: John Wagner & Alan Grant
Art: Ron Smith

Judge Dredd in "22nd Century Futsie!"
(reprint from Prog 45) Script: John Wagner
Art: Ian Gibson (6 pg)

Judge Dredd in "Exit the Dragon"   (2 pg)
Script: John Wagner & Alan Grant Art:
Matthew Jones

"The Dredd End" (1 pg) Art: Brian Bolland

TEXT STORY:
"Sweet Justice"   (8 pg) Story: Neil
Gaiman Illustrations: Lee Baulch

FEATURES:
Top of the Cops; Iso-Cube Art; The Dredd
Driving Test.

JUDGE DREDD ANNUAL
1989   £3.75

COVER: Judge Dredd by Carlos Ezquerra

COLOUR STRIPS:
Judge Dredd in "Costa Del Blood"   (29 pg)
Script: John Wagner/Alan Grant Art: Carlos
Ezquerra

BLACK & WHITE STRIPS:
Judge Dredd in "Father Earth" (reprint from
Prog 122-125) Script: John Wagner Art:
Brian Bolland/Ron Smith (23 pg)

Judge Dredd - Daily Star strip reprints
(13 pg) Script: John Wagner & Alan Grant
Art: Ron Smith

FEATURES:
Interviews - Brian Bolland, Pat Mills; Dredd
Quotations; Dredd Film Poster - Reader's
Art; Pro Files - John Wagner, Mac-1, Grant
Morrison, Alan Grant, Steve Yeowell;
Dredd Mega-Search; Cereal Thrillers; The
Mega-City Times; Dredd Rap.

JUDGE DREDD ANNUAL
1990   £3.95

COVER: Judge Dredd by John Higgins

COLOUR STRIPS:
Judge Dredd in "Stunning Stunts Club"
(6 pg) Script: Alan Grant   Art: Mark Farmer

Judge Dredd in "The Dungeon Master" (16
pg) Script: John Wagner Art: Arthur Ranson

Judge Dredd in "Brothers 'n' Arms"(7 pg)
Script: Alan Grant Art: Jeff Anderson

BLACK & WHITE STRIPS:
Judge Dredd in "Error of Judgement" (reprint
from Prog 388) Script: John Wagner Art:
Ron Smith (7 pg)

Judge Dredd - Daily Star strip reprints
(16 pg) Script: John Wagner & Alan Grant
Art: Ian Gibson

"It's a Mad, Mad, Mad World!" (5 pg)
Script: Mike Collins Art: Alan Davis

Judge Dredd in "A Case for Treatment"
(reprint from Prog 389) Script: John
Wagner Art: Ron Smith (6 pg)

Judge Dredd in "A Question of Judgement"
(reprint from Prog 387) Script: John
Wagner Art: Ron Smith (6 pg)

TEXT STORY:
"Roll on Justice" (6 pg) Story: Ian Rimmer
Illustrations: Stephen Baskerville

"Radical Cheek" (7 pg) Story: Peter Milligan
Illustrations: Jamie Hewlett

FEATURES:
Pro Files - Mark Farmer, Ron Smith, Arthur
Ranson, Alan Davis, Jeff Anderson; The
Mega-City Sport.

JUDGE DREDD ANNUAL
1991   £4.95

COVER: Judge Dredd by Jamie Hewlett

COLOUR STRIPS:
Judge Dredd in "Top Dogs" (30 pg) Script:
John Wagner Art: Colin MacNeil

BLACK & WHITE STRIPS:
Judge Dredd in "Elvis - The Killer Car"
(reprint from Progs 53-56) Script: John
Wagner Art: Ian Gibson   (24 pg)

Judge Dredd in "Jonathan Livingston Dog-
Vulture" (6 pg) Script: Alan Grant Art: Paul
Marshall

TEXT STORY:
"Exorcise Duty" (8 pg) Story: Andy
Lanning/Dan Abnett Illustrations: Anthony
Williams/ Andy Lanning

"Resyko" (8 pg) Story: John Smith
Illustrations: Sean Phillips

FEATURES:
The Sunday Meg Questionaire - John
Wagner, Alan Grant, Ian Gibson, Jamie
Hewlett, Colin MacNeil; Spec Scan - the
Lawmaster, the Lawtiver; Character Profile -
Johnny Alpha; "My Life as a Dog" - Johnny
Alpha feature; Covers of 1989.

JUDGE DREDD YEARBOOK
1992   £5.95

COVER: Judge Dredd by Dermot Power

COLOUR STRIPS:
Judge Dredd in "The Sleeper" (28 pg)
Script: John Wagner Art: Geoff Senior

Judge Dredd in "The Mystery of Judge
(Edwin Drood)"   (5 pg) Script: Dan Abnett
Art: Mike Hadley

BLACK & WHITE STRIPS:
Judge Dredd in "Back on the Streets" (reprint
from Prog 435) Script: John Wagner & Alan
Grant Art: Cam Kennedy (7 pg)

Judge Dredd in "Impact Imminent" (8
pg) Script: Simon Furman
Art: Steve

Yeowell

Judge Dredd in "Beggar's Banquet" (reprint from Prog 456) Script: John Wagner & Alan Grant Art: John Higgins (7 pg)

Judge Dredd in "Roboblock!" (8 pg) Script: Simon Furman Art: Lee Sullivan/Kev Hopgood

Judge Edwina's Strange Cases "Demonspawn" (5 pg) Script: Dave Stone Art: Kev Hopgood

TEXT STORY:
"The Most Dangerous Game" (7 pg) Story: Mark Millar Illustrations: Dermot Power

"Masquerade" (8 pg) Story: Dave Stone Illustrations: Sean Phillips

FEATURES:
Justice Dept. Rap Sheets - Geoff Senior, Cam Kennedy, Steve Yeowell, Mike Hadley, John Higgins, Lee Sullivan, Kev Hopgood; Mega-City News; 2000 I.D. - Walter the Wobot.

JUDGE DREDD YEARBOOK 1993 £5.95

COVER: Judge Dredd by Brendan McCarthy

COLOUR STRIPS:
Judge Dredd in "Serial Killer" (23 pg) Script: John Wagner Art: Simon Hunter

Soul Sisters in "The Dark Nuns Return" (7 pg) Script: David Bishop/Dave Stone Art: Shaky Kane

BLACK & WHITE STRIPS:
Judge Anderson in "George" (5 pg) Script: Alan Grant Art: Russell Fox

Red Razors in "Doctor's Orders" (7 pg) Script: Mark Millar Art: Steve Yeowell

Judge Dredd in "Atlantis" (reprint from Progs 485-488) Script: John Wagner Art: Brendan McCarthy (22 pg)

The Straitjacket Fits: "The Final Fit" (5 pg) Script: David Bishop Art: Roger Langridge

Judge Joyce in "When Irish Pies are Smiling" (7 pg) Script: Garth Ennis Art: Steve Dillon

TEXT STORY:
Armitage in "The Case of the Detonating Dowager" (4 pg) Story: Dave Stone Illustrations: Sean Phillips

FEATURES:
Characters Files - Judge Anderson, Red Razors, Soul Sisters, Armitage, Straitjacket Fits, Judge Joyce; Feature - Democracy, What the Papers Said; Pin-up - Brit-Cit Babes.

JUDGE DREDD YEARBOOK 1994 £5.95

COVER: Judge Dredd, Mean Machine, Judge

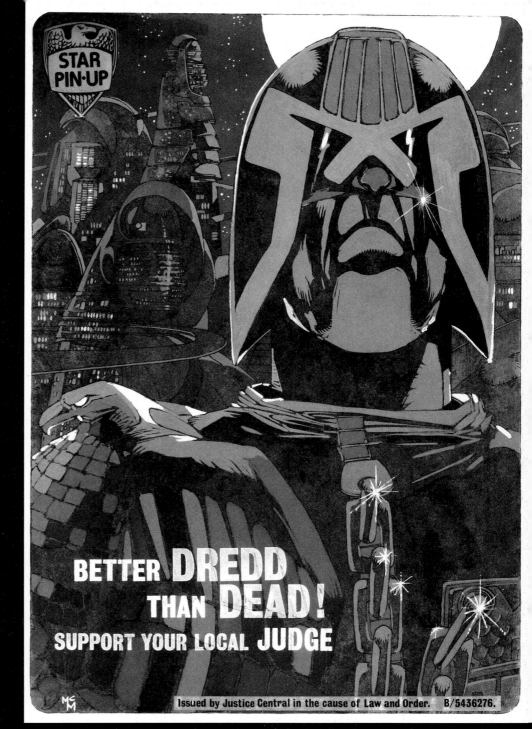

STAR PIN·UP

BETTER DREDD THAN DEAD!
SUPPORT YOUR LOCAL JUDGE

Issued by Justice Central in the cause of Law and Order. B/5436276.

COLOUR STRIPS:
Judge Dredd in "Nightmare Man" (16 pg) Script: Alan Grant Art: Dean Ormston

Judge Dredd in "Spoc's Mock Chocs" (reprint from Prog 614) Script: Alan Grant Art: Brendan McCarthy & Jamie Hewlett (6 pg)

Judge Hershey in "Naked and Unashamed" (7 pg) Script: Robbie Morrison Art: Paul Peart

Judge Dredd in "Breakdown on 9th Street" (reprint from Progs 620, 621) Script: John Wagner Art: John Higgins (12 pg)

BLACK & WHITE STRIPS:

Mean Machine in "Judgement on Gosham" (10 pg) Script: John Wagner Art: Mike McMahon

Armitage in "The Fall of the House of Toddler" (21 pg) Script: Dave Stone Art: Russell Fox

TEXT STORY:
Devlin Waugh in "Body and Soul" (9 pg) Story: John Smith Illustrations: Sean Phillips

FEATURES:
Characters Files - Mean Machine, Judge Hershey, Armitage, Devlin Waugh; Features - Judge Dredd annuals and yearbooks index; Death and Life of Mean Machine Angel

12 THINGS YOU NEVER KNEW ABOUT JUDGE DREDD ANNUALS AND YEARBOOKS!

1 The 1981 Judge Dredd Annual was a landmark edition for several reasons. It is the only annual or yearbook (to date) to include not a single page of reprint material, because of IPC's 5-year reprint rule (see first page of this feature)!

2 The 1981 annual featured the very first Judge Dredd story, which had never been published in the pages of 2000 AD. The five-page story about Dredd foiling a bank robbery was written by John Wagner and drawn by Carlos Ezquerra!

3 The 1981 annual also featured a Walter's Robo-Tale called Shok!, by Steve MacManus and Kevin O'Neill. The story inspired a British science fiction film, Hardware, ten years later. MacManus and O'Neill receive a special credit in the very last frame of the film!

4 The 1983 annual included the story The Mean Machine Gets Married!, by Alan Grant and Robin Smith. Mean Machine Angel meets and marries Seven-Pound Sadie Suggs, so named because she robs banks using a seven-pound hammer. A ten-part story which picks up the threads of this tale and reintroduces Seven-Pound Sadie is coming soon in Judge Dredd The Megazine. The title? Son of Mean Machine!

5 The 1983 annual also interviews writer T. B. Grover, alias John Wagner. A John Wagner pro file appeared in the 1988 annual and a questionnaire in the 1991 annual, making him the most-profiled creator of all!

6 Carlos Ezquerra has contributed the most pages by an artist to Judge Dredd annuals. His 143 pages (most of them colour) is nearly triple the total of his nearest rivals, Mike McMahon (58 pages) and John Higgins (38 pages). The artist to contribute the least pages is Brian Bolland with only 2!

7 The 1986 annual is the only one which didn't include credit cards, naming the writer, artist and letterer for each of the stories inside. Our special index reveals the creators involved for the very first time!

8 Carlos Ezquerra has also painted the most covers with four (1984, 85, 86 and 89) of his works as cover, while Brian Bolland and John Higgins have each contributed two covers for the annuals and yearbooks!

9 The 1988 annual features a Judge Hershey text story, written by Neil Gaiman. He has since become a bestselling fantasy author and writer of the multi-award-winning comic book series Sandman for America's DC Comics company!

10 The 1989 annual is the only one to not include a te: story. These short stories have been long been a traditional aspect of annuals. A series of all new Judge Dredd fiction novels is planned for 1993!

11 The longest story ever to appear in a Judge Dredd annual was the 30-pager Top Dogs, by John Wagne and Colin MacNeil, in the 1991 annual. Strontium Dogs Johnny Alpha and Wulf travel back in time to capture a fugitive hiding in Mega-City One. Johnny and Dredd have a massive fistfight, which had its sequel when they were forced collaborate during the 1992 mega-epic Judgement Day!

12 The shortest stories ever in an annual were both on page long and both drawn by Brian Bolland. The fi was an untitled Walter the Wobot story in the 1986 annual and the second was The Dredd End in the 1988 annual Bolland also scripted The (controversial) Dredd End!

JUDGE DREDD

SPOK'S MOCK CHOCS

MOCK CHOC!

ON MAY 10th 2111, SUBJECT AC-B14317 (HENRY) PASSED AWAY, AGED TWO YEARS AND ONE MONTH.

HENRY, WHO IN THE COURSE OF HIS SHORT LIFE HAD EATEN 1,520 CHUNKY ALL-SYNTHETIC CHOK-BARS, WAS HALFWAY THROUGH THE 1,521st WHEN THE END CAME —

SCRIPT
G. GRANT
ART R-MC²
HEWLETT, WHITAKER
LETTERING
T. FRAME

HEWLETT   R-MC²   WHITAKER

MEAN MACHINE:
Judgement on Gosham

Script: JOHN WAGNER
Art: MIKE McMAHON
Lettering: GORDON ROBSON

Some jobs are too dangerous,
even for the Judges of Mega-City
One. You need someone that's
bloodthirsty, violent and - most
of all - expendable. Enter Mean
Machine...

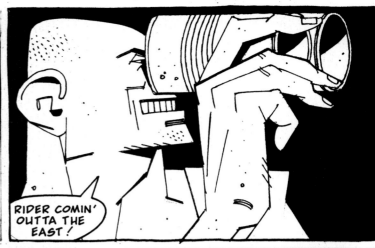

OUR STORY BEGINS A FEW HOURS EARLIER, FAR TO THE EAST IN MEGA-CITY ONE--

ON CONSIDERATION WE FEEL WE'VE MADE CERTAIN *MISTAKES* WITH YOUR TREATMENT, MEAN. WE MUST ADOPT A MORE *POSITIVE* APPROACH, ENCOURAGE YOU TO BECOME A USEFUL MEMBER OF SOCIETY, HELP YOU TO REALISE YOUR FULL POTENTIAL.

NOBODY HELPS ME TA REALISE MY FULL POTENTIAL LESS'N I SEZ THEY CAN!

psy35

FOR THAT REASON WE'VE DECIDED TO MAKE YOU A *JUDGE*.

A JUDGE, HUH? YA MEAN LIKE GIVE ME POWER OVER EVERYBODY? I CAN BUTT TH' WHOLE *CITY* TO A PULP IF'N I WANTS TA?

THAT'S CORRECT.

WELL, THAT'S DIFF'RENT! WHAR DO I SIGN?

MEAN TRIES ON THE UNIFORM—

RRRIPP!

FITS LIKE A STINKIN' GLOVE!

WHEN CAN I START KILLIN'?

NOT SO FAST! BEFORE YOU CAN TAKE YOUR PLACE ON THE STREETS WE HAVE TO DO A TEST TO MAKE SURE YOU'RE *FIT* TO BE A JUDGE.

'COURSE I'S FIT TO BE A JUDGE! I'S A PSYCHOPATHIC *MANIAC*, AIN'T I?

IF YOU WANT TO BE A JUDGE, YOU'RE JUST GOING TO HAVE TO GO ALONG WITH US ON THIS ONE.

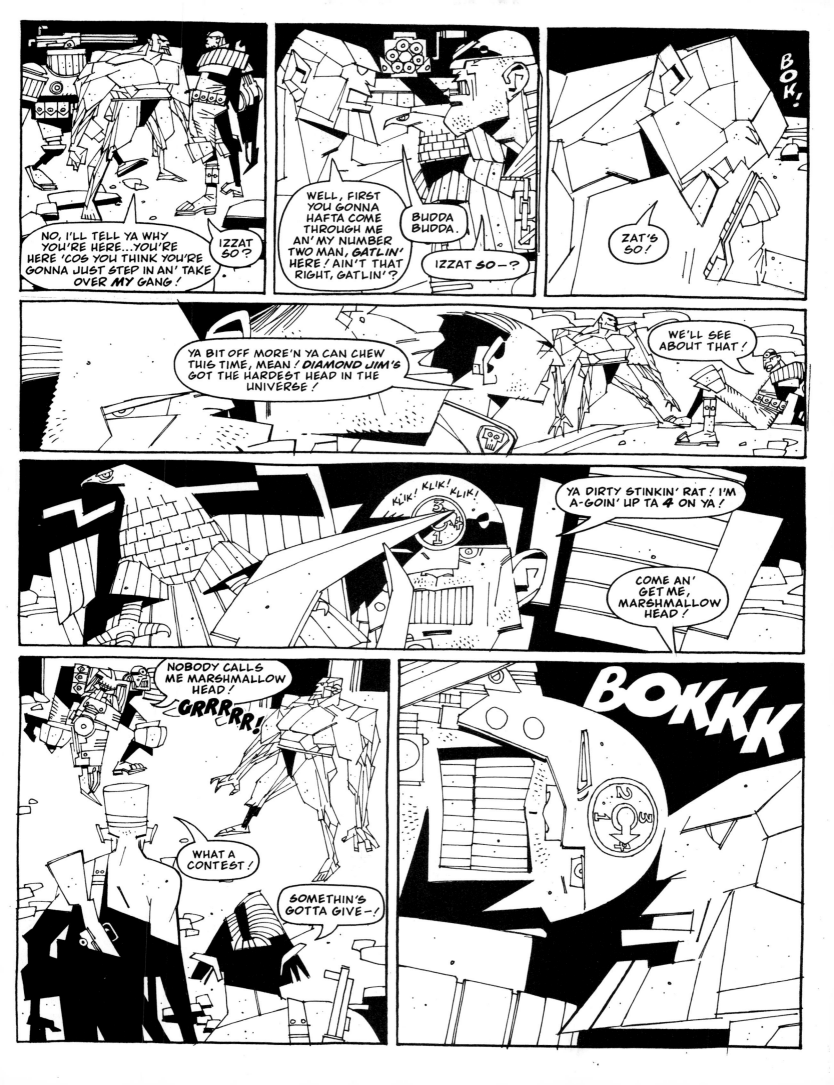

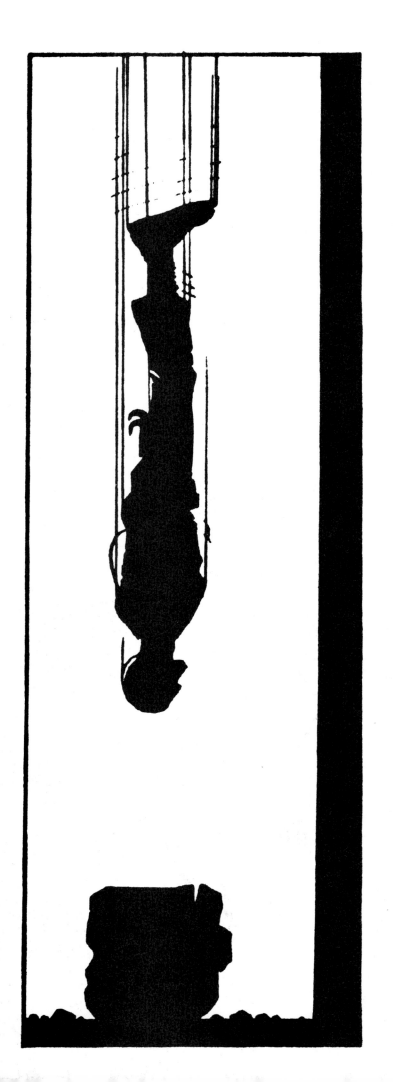

MEAN! SURLY! VICIOUS! BRUTAL!

A psychological profile on Mean Machine Angel, Compiled by Doctor A. Potter BSc BMed University of Mega-City One.

MEAN AND MOODY: Mean Machine Angel executes a copybook divebutt (left), image by Robin Smith; a rare image of the notorious Angel Gang (far right), by Mike McMahon.

MEAN MACHINE Angel is one of the most dangerous criminals ever to plague the Judges of Mega-City One. Fortunately, he is also one of the most stupid!

Aside from the occasional, short-lived escapes from captivity, Mean Machine has been held in iso-cubes for most of the past ten years. During that time he has been subject to repeated attempts at rehabilitation, including brain surgery, drug treatments and hypnotism.

It was while hypnotised that Mean revealed much of the information contained in this profile.

Born and raised in the Cursed Earth, Mean as a child was actually kind, friendly and helpful to others. At age twelve he liked pretty flowers with their nice colours, birds, butterflies, bees and rabbits. He especially loved rabbits and had his own pet rabbit - until it was butchered by one of his brothers, Link Angel.

Young Mean had a problem - he was the white sheep of the Angel family. Everybody else was nasty, vicious, murderous and generally unpleasant.

His eldest brother, Fink Angel, was 'real crazy' according to Mean, living in a hole in the ground next to the family homestead from the age of seven

and poisoning any unfortunate passing strangers.

Link Angel was 'too dumb to know how bad he was, but he was real bad too'. It was Link who practised some vivisection techniques on the young Mean's pet rabbit with an axe.

Junior Angel was the baby of the family, but the most evil of them all. All three of Mean's siblings used their weak, good-natured brother for target practice, terrifying the young boy.

Sadly, it seems parental misguidance was the main cause of this family's criminal behaviour tendencies. Mean's father - Elmer 'Pa' Angel - egged the children on, urging them to be bad.

Nothing is known of Mean's mother, except that she killed a hundred and thirty-four men with her bare hands! Any woman who could commit such atrocities and give birth to such dangerous offspring is obviously a menace to society at large. We can only hope that this terrible woman is now dead.

TRAGIC TURNING POINT!

At age 13, the tragic turning point of Mean Machine Angel's life took place, when his father kidnapped a top surgeon from Texas City and forced him to operate on the young boy.

Despite cries of pain and protest, Mean's left arm was cut off and replaced with a robotic arm, with a metal claw. A dial was welded into Mean's head with four settings aligned to his mental state - ranging from mean (setting 1), to surly (2), vicious (3) and brutal (4).

Together with some

JUDGE DREDD IS A DEAD MAN!

crude brain surgery, this made Mean the most dangerous and virtually unstoppable head-butter in history. Now Mean Machine was truly a member of the Angel family!

The boys all grew up and their father, Pa Angel, formed them into one of the Cursed Earth's most notorious and feared forces for evil - the Angel Gang. (Fink Angel did not join the gang, preferring to stay in his hole, developing newer, deadlier poisons.)

Mean and the rest of the gang terrorised local townships and often smashed their way into nearby Texas City, looting, burning and pillaging.

For his twenty-first birthday, Mean Machine was given the key to a safe deposit box in the First Bank of Tex. After being driven to the outskirts of the city by his siblings, Mean broke into the closed bank and tried to headbutt his way into the safe deposit box (the door was on a timelock).

When it resisted all efforts, he finally took it to the top of the building, threw it out the window, then threw himself out after it - a fifty story divebutt!

Inside the demolished cabinet he found a special gift - a box of Mutie Tray chocolates. Mean was captured and spent the next two years in a Texas City iso-cube, trying to butt his way out, until his family sprung him from jail.

MEAN MACHINE GETS MARRIED!

Soon afterwards, Mean met the woman of his dreams - Sarah 'Seven-Pound-Sadie' Suggs, so named because of the seven-pound hammer she wields. They first met when Mean butted his way into a Texas bank, intent on violent crime - but Sadie was already robbing it. She hit him with her hammer and escaped, while Mean was left dazed and smitten - love at first smash.

After some wooing and canoodling, the date for their marriage was set. The Angel Gang used the wedding as an excuse to extort 'wedding presents' - minimum value 50 creds - from the local population. The marriage went ahead but before the honeymoon could begin, Sadie duped Mean into knocking himself out and she stole away with all the loot, never to be seen again!

The gang next came to the attention of the authorities in a bizarre case of cross-time terror, when an older Mean travelled back in time and brought

his father and brothers forward to the year 2113 AD - but more on that dangerous, eternity-threatening episode later.

Eventually the gang was captured and imprisoned in Texas City, but in 2102 AD they broke out of jail again. Pa, Mean, Link and Junior kidnapped the Judge Child, a powerful psychic sought by Mega-City One lawman, Judge Dredd. The gang decided to go off-world to avoid recapture, and escaped from earth in a hijacked space craft. Dredd followed in the Justice One spacecraft.

After a long chase, Dredd tracked the gang down to the barren volcanic planet Xanadu, on the far edge of the Johannsen Cluster. This was a lawless planet, offering refuge to the galaxy's worst fugitives.

Pa Angel sent Mean and Link to kill Dredd, but the lawman shot Mean's right arm off. 'Lucky it was only me real one!' is Mean's incredible recollection of the event.

THE DEATH OF MEAN MACHINE!

During the conflict Mean's dial got stuck on four and a half, driving him into an uncontrollable butt frenzy. It ceased only when Mean butted into two petrol pumps, killing himself and Link in the resulting explosion.

(Dredd later executed Junior Angel but Pa was killed by the Judge Child. Dredd decided the child was evil and left it stranded on Xanadu.)

News of the Angel Gang's demise spread back to earth and Fink Angel emerged from his hole in the ground, seeking revenge against the crew members of Justice One. He was eventually captured by Dredd and cubed for life.

Two years after his death, Mean Machine Angel was alive again. The Judge Child resurrected Mean using regeneration elixirs, while using his vast mental powers to help Fink Angel escape from his cube in Iso-Block 666. The Judge Child sent Mean back to Earth to be reunited with Fink and seek revenge on Dredd.

The two Angels teamed up and attacked Dredd's conapt in Rowdy Yates Block. Mean butted Dredd's mechanoid servant, Walter the Wobot, to pieces and kidnapped the

LOVE AND FAMILY: Mean Machine Angel pictured on his wedding day with Sadie Angel (nee Suggs - above), image by Robin Smith; below, a family portrait of the Angel Gang - the photographer died soon after, image by Mike McMahon.

housekeeper, Maria. Dredd was lured into a trap but managed to defeat the

pair. Fink died in his special Pa Angel Mark One Super-Scream Torture Machine while Mean went back to the cubes.

Two years on in 2106 AD, Mean was brainwashed into believing Judge Dredd was actually his Pa. Dredd needed a guide to the radlands north of Texas City - Angel Gang country! The brainwashing eventually wore off and Dredd only survived by shooting off both Mean's kneecaps. The supreme buttist went back to the cubes...

(By this time in his life, a pattern was developing. Mean would escape the cubes or be subjected to some new form of rehabilitation. But he always reverted to his old ways - it seems his family conditioning overwhelms any and all attempts at making him into a better citizen.)

MEAN'S HATRED CAN NEVER DIE!

By Christmas of 2107, the doctors working on his case had given up on subtlety and simply gave him a full frontal lobotomy, seemingly removing all traces of aggression. The treatment seemed so successful the now totally passive Mean was let out on day release to a Mr and Mrs Puddock. But a series of cruel jokes tipped him back over into psychotic behaviour. The surgeons had removed his frontal lobes, but they could never remove the hatred! Mean was recaptured by Dredd after the hate-crazed fugitive butted a terrorist who had five kilos of hi-ex strapped to his body! The terrorist died but Mean lived on to be cubed again. Having died once already, Mean now seemed virtually invulnerable.

The only surviving member of the Angel Gang disappeared for several years, while he underwent long, arduous sessions of hypnotherapy. Finally in 2113 he emerged again, as a demonstration subject for Professor Wally Dingbert, of the University of Mega-City One. Dingbert was confident he had cured the Mean Machine at last. Unfortunately, some Mega-U students tricked the now docile Mean into petty crime and the panicking Angel decided to hide in a lecture theatre. There he was exposed to the side effects of a prototype time machine's oscillations, which undid all the post-hypnotic suggestions.

Mean hijacked the time machine and travelled back in time to warn his family about their impending deaths at the hands of Judge Dredd and the Judge Child. The whole Angel Gang (now made up of two Mean Machines - old and young!) took control of the time machine and eventually turned up in 2113, where they were subdued by Judge Dredd.

The original gang had all memories of the time travelling burned out of their brains and were returned to their own time, while Mean went back to the cubes again.

His next escapade involved the alien superfiend Judge Death but all information on this is still subject to Justice Department secrecy measures and was not available for inclusion in this study.

It is obvious that Mean Machine Angel is impossible to rehabilitate and all attempts should be abandoned, as they only lead to disaster. I recommend he simply be locked away forever in the most secure cube available - if he escapes again, who knows what havoc could happen?

LIFE AND DEATH: Mean Machine Angel goes into an uncontrollable and fatal butt-frenzy on Xanadu (above), image by Mike McMahon; Mean lives again, thanks to the Judge Child, image by Carlos Ezquerra (below).

MEAN MACHINE ANGEL
Art by Chris Halls

JUDGE HERSHEY:
Naked and Unashamed

Script: ROBBIE MORRISON
Art: PAUL PEART
Lettering: GORDON ROBSON

Nudists are a friendly bunch.
When Mega-City One's first
nudist block opens, it sounds to
good to be true. And it is too
good to be true, as Judge
Hershey soon discovers...

THERE'S MORE TO NUDISM THAN MEETS THE EYE --

Aaaahhhh --

IT'S MORE THAN JUST A PHYSICAL THING --

DESSERT, DEAR?

Mmmm --

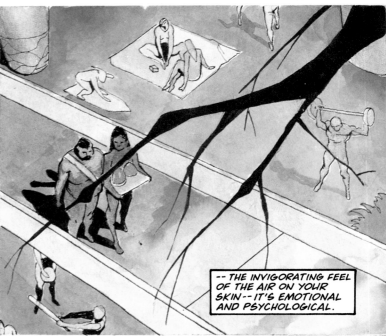

-- THE INVIGORATING FEEL OF THE AIR ON YOUR SKIN -- IT'S EMOTIONAL AND PSYCHOLOGICAL.

NUDISM'S HONEST AND FREE, STRIPPING AWAY HUMAN COMPLEXES AND SOCIETY'S INDOCTRINATION.

-- NASTY RASH YOU'VE GOT --

-- SORRY, JUST CAN'T EAT HOT DOGS, NOWADAYS --

-- WATER RETENTION --

NUDISTS HAVE NO SECRETS, NOTHING TO HIDE.

IF ALL THE CITIZENS IN ALL THE WORLD WERE NUDISTS, IT'D BE A HAPPIER PLACE.

IN MEGA-CITY ONE, WHEN YOU STRIP AWAY HUMAN COMPLEXES AND SOCIAL INDOCTRINATION, THERE'S ONLY *ONE* THING LEFT--

NO! DON'T--

AAIIEEE!!

--NAKED JUSTICE.

SOON...

I SUPPOSE YOU NEED *THIS* BACK, JUDGE HERSHEY?

CONTROL? MED UNITS AND MEAT WAGONS NEEDED AT RUSS MEYER BLOCK.

OH, AND HAVE THEM BRING ME A *NEW* HELMET FROM STORES!

THE END.

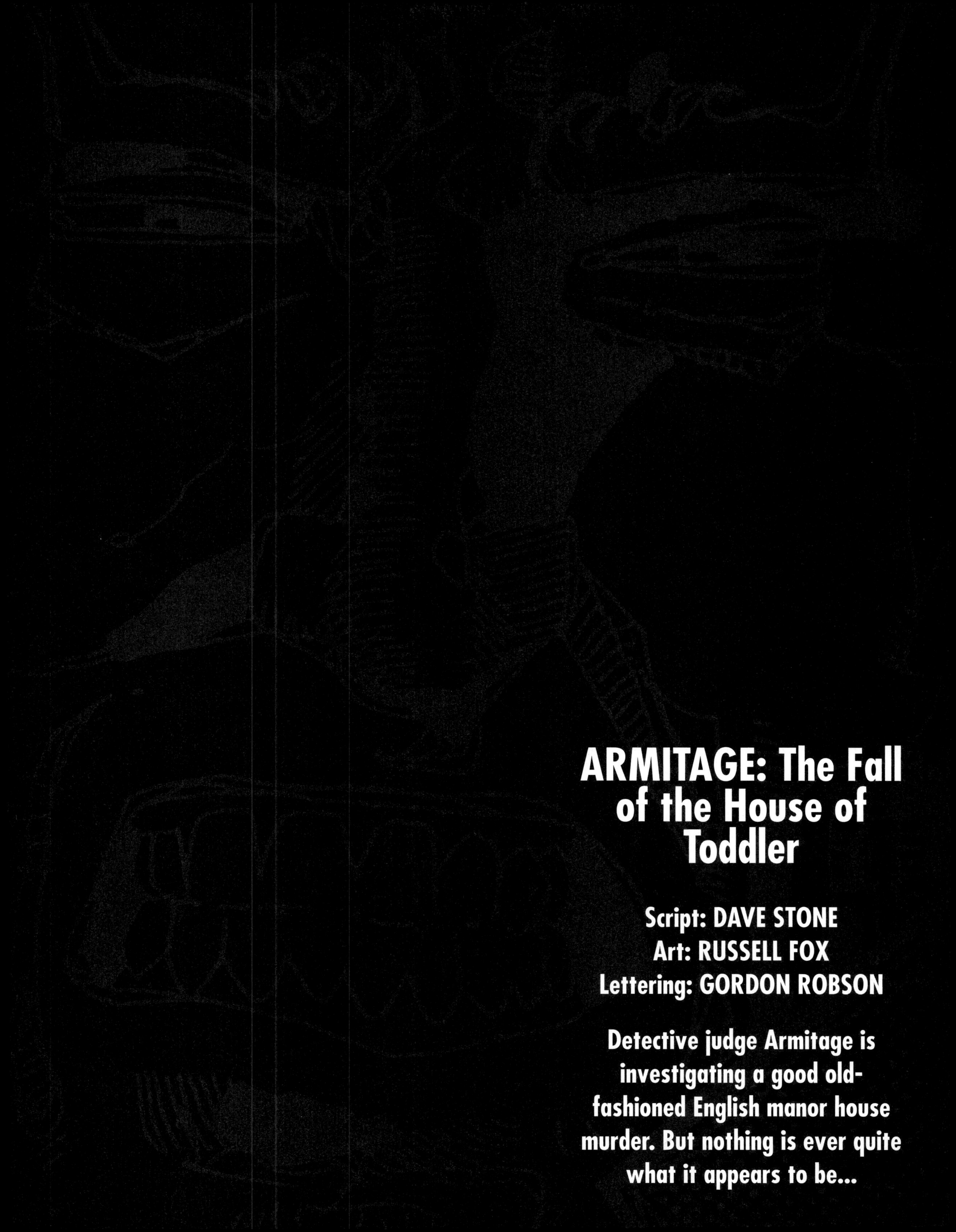

ARMITAGE: The Fall of the House of Toddler

Script: DAVE STONE
Art: RUSSELL FOX
Lettering: GORDON ROBSON

Detective judge Armitage is
investigating a good old-
fashioned English manor house
murder. But nothing is ever quite
what it appears to be...

BRIT-CIT, 2114 AD.
NEW OLD BAILEY.

PLEASE!

HELP ME PLEASE!

LOOK, WILL YOU JUST CALM DOWN?! WHAT ARE YOU TRYING TO--

NO TIME! NO TIME LEFT AT ALL!

THEY'RE COMING FOR ME, CREEPING UP THE STAIRS AND--

WHARK!

CHUNKA! CHUNKA! CHUNKA! CHUNKA!

THAT'S... THAT'S HORRIBLE. THE NEW OLD BAILEY CLEAR-UP RATE'S BAD ENOUGH AS IT IS!

GET ME DETECTIVE JUDGE ARMITAGE, NOW.

HE'S GONE WALKABOUT, SIR. NOBODY'S SEEN HIM FOR DAYS.

WELL, GET ME THAT GIRL OF HIS THEN! STEEL OR WHATEVER HER NAME IS...

"...I'M SURE **SHE** CAN FIND WHATEVER ROCK HE'S CRAWLED UNDER."

ARMITAGE?

YOU'RE WANTED ON A CASE. THIS IS **WORK**, ARMITAGE!

DROKK OFF AND LEAVE ME ALONE...

OKAY.

YOU DON'T LEAVE ME ANY **CHOICE**.

CHUNK! TSSSS

GLURP!

Ye Toilet

DROKK ME! WHAT WAS I **DRINKING** LAST NIGHT..?

EVERYTHING, BY THE LOOK OF IT.

...SO THE VICTIM WAS ONE *BARNABAS TODDLER*, ONE OF YOUR ACTUAL LANDED GENTRY.

WE TRACED THE CALL TO HIS *ANCESTRAL HOME* IN THE EASTERN AGRISECTOR...

EASTERN AGRISECTOR

...TODDLER GRANGE.

THEY DON'T BUILD 'EM LIKE THAT ANYMORE.

SO WHAT'S THE STORY, SERGEANT?

OI REALLY COULDN'T SAY, ZUR.

THEY DO SAY AS 'OW THERE BE *STRANGE A'GOIN'S ON* IN THAT THERE 'OUSE—AN' OI IN'T A'GOIN' IN FOR NEITHER LOVE NOR MONEY!

YOU'M ON YOUR OWN THERE, BOI.

SUIT YOURSELF. MOUNT A GUARD AROUND THE PLACE, AND HAND YOUR BADGE IN AT THE SECTOR HOUSE WHEN YOU GO.

ROIT Y'ARE, ZUR!

BAM! BAM! BAM!

JUSTICE DEPARTMENT! OPEN UP!

CAN I HELP YOU AT ALL?

DETECTIVE JUDGE ARMITAGE. MY ASSOCIATE, TREASURE STEEL.

BRIT-CIT JUSTICE DEPT
Detective Judge Armitage

WE'RE INVESTIGATING MURDER.

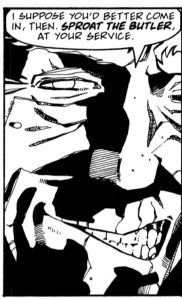

I SUPPOSE YOU'D BETTER COME IN, THEN. SPROAT THE BUTLER, AT YOUR SERVICE.

YOU'RE JUST IN TIME FOR SUPPER.

THE FAMILY WILL BE GATHERED IN THE DINING ROOM.

ALLOW ME TO PRESENT THE TODDLERS OF TODDLER GRANGE!

"LADY HONORIA TODDLER...

CHARMED, I'M SURE.

"...HER OFFSPRING, D'ARCY AND JACQUINTA...

WHAT AN ODD LITTLE MAN.

EH, WOT?

"...AND UNCLE SMEDLEY!"

I HAD EGGS FOR TEA.

AND TO WHAT DO WE OWE THIS PLEASURE?

WE HAVE A VIDEOCALL SHOWING ONE BARNABAS TODDLER BRUTALLY SHREDDED BY A LASER-RAZOR.

WE SUSPECT FOUL PLAY.

MY HUSBAND?

HOW DARE YOU!

I'LL HAVE YOU KNOW THAT BARNABAS IS ALIVE AS YOU OR I!

HE'S UP HERE, IN HIS STUDY, WORKING UPON HIS MEMOIRS.

WHY, HE CALLED DOWN FOR TIFFIN NOT FIVE HOURS AGO!

SHORTLY...

OKAY...SO HERE'S HOW IT HAPPENED...

THE STAIRWELL LEADING TO TODDLER'S STUDY WAS BOOBY-TRAPPED—AND HIS REMAINS WERE THE *BAIT*.

THE TRAP WAS TRIPPED BY A PRESSURE SWITCH IN THE STUDY ITSELF, SO THE FIRST PERSON TO LEAVE IT WOULD *ALSO* DIE.

THAT MEANS, EXCEPT FOR THE MURDERER, THAT *ALL* OF YOU WERE POTENTIAL VICTIMS...

RAAAK!

BZZZT!

PLINK!

TYPICAL.

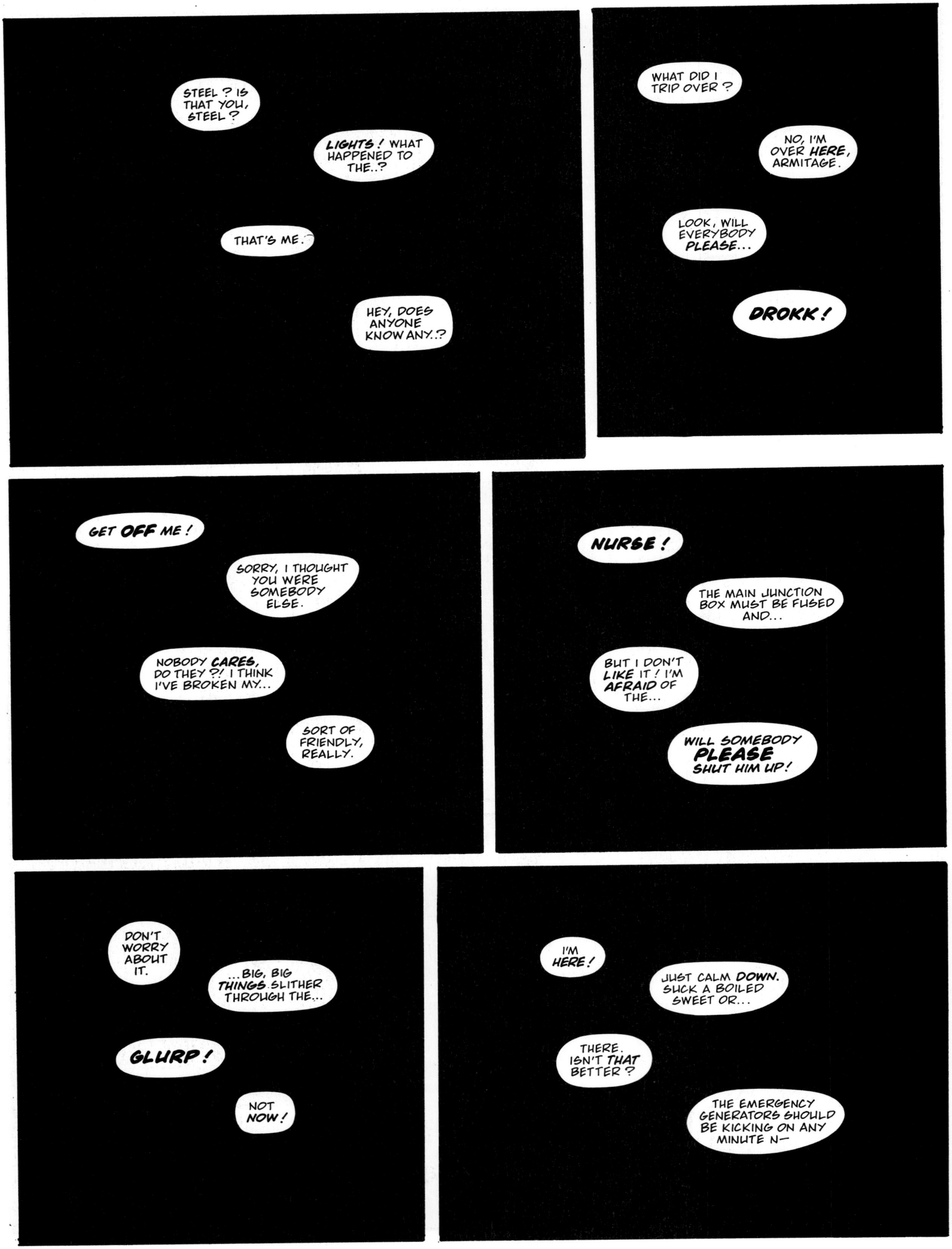
STEEL ? IS THAT YOU, STEEL ?
LIGHTS ! WHAT HAPPENED TO THE..?
THAT'S ME.
HEY, DOES ANYONE KNOW ANY..?
WHAT DID I TRIP OVER ?
NO, I'M OVER HERE, ARMITAGE.
LOOK, WILL EVERYBODY PLEASE...
DROKK !
GET OFF ME !
SORRY, I THOUGHT YOU WERE SOMEBODY ELSE.
NOBODY CARES, DO THEY ?! I THINK I'VE BROKEN MY...
SORT OF FRIENDLY, REALLY.
NURSE !
THE MAIN JUNCTION BOX MUST BE FUSED AND...
BUT I DON'T LIKE IT ! I'M AFRAID OF THE...
WILL SOMEBODY PLEASE SHUT HIM UP!
DON'T WORRY ABOUT IT.
...BIG, BIG THINGS SLITHER THROUGH THE...
GLURP !
NOT NOW !
I'M HERE !
JUST CALM DOWN. SUCK A BOILED SWEET OR...
THERE. ISN'T THAT BETTER ?
THE EMERGENCY GENERATORS SHOULD BE KICKING ON ANY MINUTE N—

THANK DROKK FOR THAT.

NOW SHUT UP THE *LOT* OF YOU SO I CAN—

ARMITAGE...

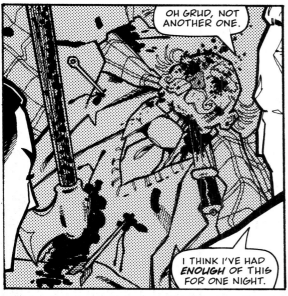

OH GRUD, NOT ANOTHER ONE.

I THINK I'VE HAD *ENOUGH* OF THIS FOR ONE NIGHT.

I'D SUGGEST YOU TWO *RETIRE* BEFORE I DESPATCH THE PAIR OF YOU *MYSELF*. IT MIGHT BE AN IDEA IF YOU LOCK YOUR DOORS.

THERE'S AN ARMED GUARD AROUND THE HOUSE—SO DON'T EVEN *THINK* ABOUT LEAVING.

YOU, *SCROAT* OR WHATEVER YOUR NAME IS. MAKE ME UP A BED.

VERY GOOD, SIR.

ARMITAGE, IF YOU THINK I'M GOING TO *SLEEP* IN THIS PLACE...

DON'T WORRY ABOUT IT.

"WHO SAID ANYTHING ABOUT *YOU SLEEPING*?"

Z

DAWN, AND ARMITAGE RESUMES HIS INVESTIGATIONS...

...FINALLY LOCATING D'ARCY TODDLER IN HIS ROOFTOP HOTHOUSE.

ARE YOU TRYING TO **EVADE** ME, TODDLER?

NOTHING OF THE **SORT**, DETECTIVE!

SOME OF THESE ALIEN PLANT-FORMS NEED CONSTANT CARE AND ATTENTION.

WHY, MY **SENTIENT VENUSIAN FLESH-FENSERS** ARE THE PRIDE OF GARDEN FETES FROM HERE TO—

uh...

YUM!

SNUFFLES?

YUM YUM YUM!

SNUFFLES! WHAT'S COME **OVER** YOU?

YUM-YUM-YUM!

YUM!

oh strom.

KA-FOOM!

POOR D'ARCY. I **TOLD** HIM HE SHOULD HAVE STUCK WITH THE **KNIPHOFIA UVARIA**.

I MEAN, YOU **NEVER** GET THIS SORT OF TROUBLE WITH A RED-HOT AFRICAN POKER...

SEEMS TO ME THE SUSPECTS HAVE JUST NARROWED TO A FIELD OF **TWO**.

YOU DON'T SAY.

BEEP! BEEP! BEEP!

EXCUSE ME ONE MOMENT!

IF YOU ASK ME, IT'S OPEN-AND-SHUT, ARMITAGE. SHE'S THE ONLY ONE LEFT!

JACQUINTA TODDLER, I'M ARRESTING YOU FOR THE MURDERS OF...

HANG ON, STEEL.

THERE'S SOMETHING SLIGHTLY ODD ABOUT THIS...

HYDRAULIC FLUID.

SEEMS OUR BUTLER HERE IS A CYBORG.

OF COURSE SPROAT WAS A CYBORG. WHAT DID YOU THINK HE WAS?

I MEAN, YOU CAN'T GET THE HELP, NOWADAYS...

SHRED MATIC

THEN WHAT WAS THE POINT OF —?

EXACTLY, DETECTIVE...

...NO POINT...

NO POINT AT **ALL**!

GASP! DADDY..!

WHAT THE DROKK..?

SHK-KK!

BONK

D-DADDY? YOU'RE **ALIVE**?

NOT AT ALL, MY DEAR.

I'M DEAD AS THE PROVERBIAL DOORNAIL. THIS IS AN **INTERACTIVE SIMULATION**, MORE-OR-LESS PRODUCING MY REACTIONS.

I COULD HAVE JUST MADE A HOLO-VID, OF COURSE — BUT ONE DOES ENJOY A GOOD **GLOAT**.

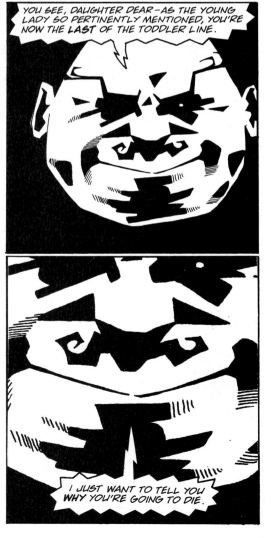

YOU SEE, DAUGHTER DEAR — AS THE YOUNG LADY SO PERTINENTLY MENTIONED, YOU'RE NOW THE **LAST** OF THE TODDLER LINE.

I JUST WANT TO TELL YOU WHY YOU'RE GOING TO DIE.

SCRATCH ONE PROBLEM.

LET'S GET THE DROKK *OUT* OF HERE, STEEL !

BZZZT! BZZZT!

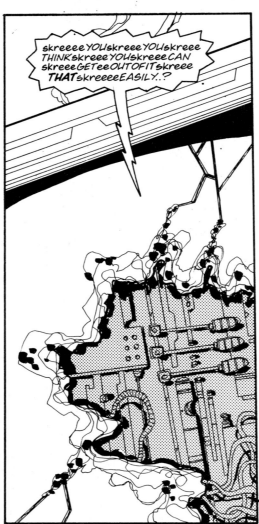

skreeee YOUskreee YOUskreee THINKskreee YOUskreee CAN skreee GETee OUT OF IT skreee *THAT* skreeee EASILY..?

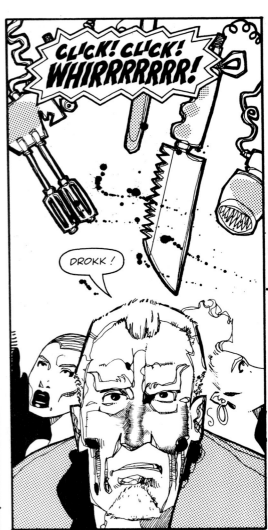

CLICK! CLICK! WHIRRRRRRR!

DROKK !

SKRAASH!

HEY, LISTEN, DON'T YOU THINK HE'D HAVE *BOOBY-TRAPPED* THE FRONT DOOR ?

GRUD ALONE KNOWS !

I WOULDN'T PUT IT *PAST* HIM.

RRRRRRRRR

THE END.

DEVLIN WAUGH:
Body and Soul

Text: JOHN SMITH
Illustrations: SEAN PHILLIPS

Devlin Waugh is unique. A freelance exorcist and papal envoy, he is infected with a vampirism virus. While recuperating on the Riviera he encounters the bizarre, and very deadly Mr Chigley...

I am Mr Chigley. The stillborn son. The white in the eye. I walk the streets and I am right here with you. You are mine. There is nothing you can do.

'**G**et me a double seafood pizza with potato salad and extra anchovies,' Haines shouted to Alvarez across the white striplit plaza. 'And don't forget the lady's sourbread.'

It was going on seven o'clock, getting dark out, the sky over the Monaco rooftops gone the colour of dead coals, and Haines hadn't eaten all day. Unless you counted the cheese and pastrami tunaburger he had for breakfast, which Haines didn't.

He wished now he'd never taken the assignment. It had sounded fun at first, almost glamorous, babysitting a movie actress on the sun-drenched Cote d'Azur. But now, standing out here on the patio of the Della Montfleury with the TV going on behind him and a kink in his belly, he was hungry for home. Missing the Euro-City nightlife, the jive, the smell on the streets.

He glanced round at the one floor red-brick apartment and in through the sliding doors. Undercover Judges popping open cans of fruit juice, big men that made the room look small. Neff and Lockhart playing cards in the corner, their first time on protective custody, enjoying having nothing to do but sit and kill time. Hagenauer over by the bathroom door, bent over polishing his shoes; Kurland sat across from the candles with a pen and puzzle book. They looked like a bunch of left-overs from yesterday's party, hangers-on hoping things might kick off again.

Haines spat into the night, that familiar cynical taste back in his mouth. What the hell was **he** bitching for? He was **one** of them. Judge Pablo Haines, half-Cuban, half-Welsh, looking sharp in tan slacks and loafers, a white cotton shirt with yellow fruit on. Eighteen years as a Judge: twelve on the streets, the last six in undercover. The sudden change he blamed on the uniform; he liked being a Judge but hated the shoulder-pads, the regulation boots, the helmet that was like looking through a letterbox.

Kurland came out onto the porch and slumped down in one of the rattan patio chairs. Psi-Judge Louis Kurland, Lou to his friends, with his tattooed forearms and weird albino looks. Wearing RapideReact sunglasses and a blue and red baseball cap that was kind of a trademark.

'Jesus. That woman.' Kurland shook his head and took a long sip of iced tea. 'She's inna bathroom takin' a shower, we're thinkin' we got maybe a few minutes peace, suddenly this voice comes waverin' outta there, "Excuse me, but could one of you officers possibly scrub my back for me?" Real life an' she still acts like she's in one a them lousy drokkin' movies a hers.'

Haines gave him a sad smile. 'She gets to you, doesn't she?'

'Man, she'd get to my great Uncle Elvin, an' he's been dead the last twelve years.'

Haines knew what he meant. Three months they'd been on this case, thirteen gruddamn weeks, and she'd been a pain in the ass from the second they picked her up. A plainclothes Judge escorting her out of the Essoldo Playhouse, into an unmarked car, then on without stopping to Sector House 23. After that they'd gone the rounds of the protective custody programme - jumping from one safehouse to another - until she'd finally insisted on coming down here.

All this for some over-the-hill movie queen who hadn't made a movie in seven years. Hadn't made a decent one in twelve. **Wildside**, which should have been her last but wasn't. Released in 2102, when they'd just brought in the new imaging technology, the AfterLife laser-constructs. Jean Fremont starring alongside Grace Kelly and Victor Mature. Being upstaged by Grace Kelly even though she was just a picture off some gruddamn machine.

'So how're we doing? Any word from Chigley yet?' Haines asked, and Kurland shrugged and told him no, no word, but not to worry, they were dug in deep, the guy'd have to be drokkin' psychic to find her out here.

This time it was Haines who shrugged. 'I don't know. Maybe he is. He found her pretty easy the last coupla times.'

Remembering that day in Ciudad Espana, a nondescript motel room like the one they were in now. A wire on the phone, round-the-clock surveillance, the works. And somehow the guy had still gotten in. Jean had woken up that morning to find tropical fish stapled to the walls; another of his messages scrawled on the bathroom mirror. Saying **I am Mr Chigley. The stillborn son. The white in the eye. I walk the streets and I am right there with you. Saying, You are mine. Body and soul. There is**

nothing you can do.

The guy, Chigley, had been sending Jean kook mail for twenty-three years. Telling her how he was her number one fan, how he loved her and wanted to marry her, talking to her like they were childhood friends. And now, all of a sudden, he'd gotten tired of waiting and started making moves. Saying she was his, he owned her. Saying he was coming to get her.

Haines shook his head. Jesus, just thinking about it...

'Who knows? Maybe we'll get lucky this time,' he said. Knowing there was no chance of it. Knowing sooner or later the guy would catch up with them.

It was six years since Devlin had last been gambling - seriously, anyway - and tonight he intended to lose a spectacular amount of money. He'd been drinking most of the day, holed up in a dark drawing room practising his Mongolian throat singing. Now he was thoroughly drunk, mouth dry, head spinning, and eager to lose some money. His brother Freddy had told Devlin that losing was the one thing in life he was bad at. Devlin tried to get in the practice whenever he could.

He had a hundred thousands francs on him when he came into the Casino, and was good for twice that in credit. Devlin thought he could spend a small fortune in the three, three and a half hours left before sunrise. But halfway up the sweeping marble staircase, the clatter of slot machines and roulette wheels echoing above him, he changed his mind. He ended up in the Casino restaurant. Ordered a table near the indoor fountain, spumes of water spotlit from below, and snapped his fingers at a passing waiter.

'I wonder if I might possibly trouble you for the wine list?' Slurring his words, feeling light-headed, off-centre. He watched the waiter thread his way through the tables, an Italian with slender wrists and tight shiny trousers. Devlin licked his lips and glanced round the room.

Wherever he went in Monte-Carlo, it seemed, he saw the same dreary faces. A few tables across from him a fat woman he recognised from the **Zurich Tribune** was being flattered and fed asparagus tips by four Korean bodybuilders. Over by the window was Claude deChardrey, the French cattle baron, sat with an ex-world tennis champion who ate with the wrong cutlery and picked his nose when he thought no-one was looking. The only person here of even remote interest was Jørn Rodovore, a male model from Scandinavia. Devlin had seen him around before, at Jimmy'z and Le Cygne, but never up close. Not till tonight.

Rodovore was in his early twenties, tall and lean with blond hair and blue come-to-bed eyes. The strong Aryan type. Devlin had followed his career right from the start: those early photo appearances in **Physique**, then centrespreads in **Young Adonis**. Later on his move to film and video. Seeing him here now, in the flesh, sent shivers up Devlin's spine.

'What a perfectly winsome creature.' He let out a wistful sigh. 'Perhaps I ought ask him to pose for me. Or better yet' - smiling now, getting another idea - 'invite him back to the villa for one of my midnight soirees...'

Devlin ordered from the menu, drunk by now but still making plans, running different scenes through his head. He told the waiter he'd have pistou and salad nifloise, then steak - rare, still bloody - with shallots and white tomato dressing, followed by crepe Suzette and gooseberry sorbet.

The steak was vile. Overcooked, with a texture like damp suede. Devlin demanded to see the maitre d'hotel and told him so. Telling the dapper little Frenchman that the meal was an abortion, that it looked like something you'd find on the floor of some back-street veterinarian clinic. He let the maitre d' sweat it out, listening to him agree with everything he said. Nodding and bowing, saying yes m'sieur, I cannot tell you how sorry I am, his eyes wide and frightened, knowing who Devlin was and what he could do to him. Then backing away, hurrying off to the kitchens so fast he almost tripped over twice on the way.

Rodovore had noticed the floorshow and was looking over at Devlin's table. Mouth set, face impassive, but with an inquisitive gleam in his eye. Devlin smiled brightly and gave him a little finger-wave. Drunk and hungry but feeling better already.

Devlin leaned forward and reached for his glass, bubbles hissing and popping in pink champagne. He took a long sip, savouring the taste. Moving his tongue slow and languorous over his upper canines as he watched Rodovore eat.

'What it is,' Haines was telling Kurland, both of them still on the patio in the cool September night, 'she's slept with all the right people. Hell, I wouldn't be surprised if she made it with the Chief Judge himself. You ever heard of Justice Department going to all this trouble just to protect some **actress**?'

Kurland shrugged.

'I'm telling you, that's it,' said Haines, sitting back now, sounding certain. 'Protective custody in return for sexual favours.'

Kurland didn't saying anything for a few moments, nursing his glass, those pale albino hands looking like they'd been dusted with powder. 'How long you reckon we're gonna be stuck down here?' he said finally.

Haines looked up. 'Hey, you're the Precog. You tell me.'

'Y'know, it's funny you say that,' Kurland said, folding his tattooed arms on the table. 'These last few days I been havin' my doubts. Ain't had a sniffa the six sense since we got here.'

'That unusual?'

'Bet your ass it is. Longest I ever been without gettin' a flash is two days. Normally I'll get 'em four, five, sometimes six times a day. Nothin' big, y'know,' Kurland said, 'just hints, glimpses. Like I'll see a TV show ain't gonna be on for another three hours, or maybe get to listen in on some argument I can see brewin' but which ain't happened yet. But this last week...' He took his sunglasses off, small red eyes looking at Haines across the table. 'I feel like I losta limb or somethin'.'

Haines shrugged. 'Well, the way this assignment's working out I don't think we have to worry too much.' Haines changing the subject now, trying to get onto something less personal. 'All we've done since we got here is sit on our asses eating pizza and watching TV.'

Kurland nodded, quiet all of a sudden. He reached out for the jug of iced tea and refilled his glass.

'Ask me,' Haines went on, 'this whole thing is a waste of time. All this trouble just because some two-star actress gets kinky fan mail. Some of the movies she's made, it'd be a lot stranger if she **didn't** get kinky fan mail.'

Kurland didn't say anything, his head down again like he was hunched over a crossword or a holiday brochure, reading the small print.

'You seen any of those letter yet? I'm telling you, some of them would blow your mind. I'm not kidding.'

Kurland still didn't speak. Didn't even look up. He was sat with his shoulders hunched, head low, blue watery light lapping at him from the half-open patio doors behind. Sat very still, too still. Haines watched a droplet of blood form on the tip of Kurland's nose, grow fat and heavy, and splash on the laminated table top. He felt like he should do something, touch him on the shoulder, but didn't move. The air was suddenly heavy around them, filled with a smell like hot metal.

'You getting a flash?'

Kurland nodded, getting more blood on the table. Seeing him in pain like this, Haines was glad he was with Undercover and not Psi-Division. But then Kurland was talking again, giving Haines a puzzled look, head cocked to one side. Saying 'Feathers?', making it a question, his voice different now, quiet but with an edge to it. Then nodding. 'Yes. Feathers. Feathers and blood.'

Haines pulled a handkerchief out of his pocket and passed it to him. Kurland's eyes wide. Still shiny, over-bright, but not as bad as before. He looked up at Haines, surprised, shaken.

'Jesus,' he said, shaking his head. 'Who'da thought it?'

Haines felt suddenly relieved, the tension in the air gone now, a balmy Mediterranean breeze pushing its way across the plaza. Then remembered the flash, Kurland saying feathers and blood, and knew something bad was coming.

All of a sudden not so relieved.

He gave Kurland a few seconds more, watching him take deep breaths, bring himself down. Then said, 'It's going to happen here?'

Kurland nodded.

'How long you think we've got?'

'I ain't sure. Not long. Usually, I get a flash like that, the image is all over the place. This one was clear as day.'

Off to the left, footsteps. Haines turned his head and saw Alvarez coming back from the foodbar. Boxes in his arms, piled up under his chin. Walking past the unmarked cars now, past the closed-up antiques shop where six more surveillance officers were sat with binoculars and lukewarm ginger beer. Ten judges altogether, sat out there keeping watch, not knowing that something bad was coming their way.

Haines looked over at Kurland again. 'Okay. We wait till Ms. Fremont gets finished in the bathroom, then we move out.' He pushed away from the table. 'First off, though, let's get us some of that food. I'm so hungry I could eat a leper's leg.'

After he'd finished, scooping up the last of his sorbet with a Viennese wafer, Devlin paid the bill then followed Rodovore out of the restaurant and up to the gaming rooms. High ceilings with painted murals. Stained glass and fading belle poque splendour. Roulette wheels spinning under alabaster Cupids and chandeliers like frozen waterfalls.

Devlin followed Rodovore around for a while, watching him try out the games, find one he liked, then sat at the bar as Rodovore settled down to play baccarat. Devlin ordered a brandy smash and sipped it slowly, keeping his eyes on Rodovore but letting his mind wander, seeing them in situations together, mud wrestling maybe, or a bout of fisticuffs down by the swimming pool.

The itch was back now, he realised, sitting here sipping his drink. The old blood hunger was gnawing at the edges of him, making it hard to think straight. Bright images danced through his head, reds and scarlets splashed on white, colours that made Devlin's mouth water. That was the problem with the hunger. Once it started there was only one way he could get it to stop. He could eat his way through a five-star menu and it wouldn't make any difference. Blood was the only thing that'd scratch the itch, that'd scratch both his itches at once, come to think of it.

By the time Rodovore finished at the baccarat table Devlin was too drunk and too hungry to sit still any more. He went right over to Rodovore and introduced himself.

'Jørn Rodovore, isn't it? My name's Waugh. Devlin Waugh.' He held out his hand and Rodovore shook it.

'I am happy to be meeting you, Mr Waugh.'

'Oh, Devlin, please. Surnames might be de rigueur in the rest of Europe, but here on the Riviera one must feel free to unshackle oneself of **all** social conventions. Don't you agree?'

Rodovore looked puzzled but nodded anyway. Up this close Devlin could see just how perfect his face was. Eyes like the Agean, the pale blue vein that ticked in his neck where shadows pooled like bruises. And my God, those lips, the kind of lips you wanted to bite. Just looking at him like this made the hunger shine. Devlin could feel saliva trickling out the corner of his mouth and wiped it away with a silk handkerchief.

'You're going down?' Devlin asked as they moved towards the elevator doors. Rodovore nodded. 'Then I'll escort you, if I may.'

The hunger hit again then, like someone had set off a flare in the pit of his stomach, so bad this time it doubled him up. Devlin had to reach out and take hold of Rodovore's arm just to stop himself falling over.

'I'm a quite unashamed admirer of your film work,' he was saying now, smiling but feeling like broken glass inside. 'A total devotee. Particularly of the **Matt Sterling** series. I haven't witnessed scenes of such stark sensuality since I visited the Bangkok film festival several years ago.'

The elevator bumped to a stop a few seconds later and they stepped out into the parking lot, like a big gloomy baseball pitch right under the Casino. It was cool down here, quiet too, the reserved spaces taken up by sports cars and limousines and not a single person around except them. Rodovore was talking now, telling him about the new film they were shooting in San Felix, Matt Sterling stranded on a desert island with a bunch of schoolboys, kind of an upbeat version of **Lord of the Flies**.

Devlin put a finger on Rodovore's lips. 'Hush,' he said softly, wanting to smile but not doing, afraid more saliva would come spilling out.

Rodovore looked at Devlin with those cold Scandinavian eyes, shiny and far-away now, like a deer caught in car headlights. He didn't move, didn't even blink as Devlin moved up close, ran a finger lightly down his throat, tracing a vein, his collarbone. Somewhere nearby a car horn went off, a quick sequence of notes, up and down. The theme music to **Love Story**.

'Just listen to that,' Devlin said. 'They're playing our tune.'

He moved his head forward and closed his lips around Rodovore's throat.

Haines was on his second slice of pizza when the bathroom door opened. A rush of hot air, steam and light spilling out, and there she was. Jean Fremont wet from the shower, something people'd pay money to see. A towel round her body, tanned and a little too heavy, auburn hair loose but damp. Forty-seven years old but not looking a day over forty.

She glanced round the lounge, a slow pan, taking everything in, and said, 'So when does the ball game start?'

Neff looked up from the table. 'What?'

'It's a line from a movie,' she said. '**Oneshot**. I come into the room, you guys are sat here with your shoes off, drinking beer. You look like husbands waiting for the ball game to start.'

Here we go again, thought Haines. Another gruddamn scene. Jean Fremont playing the funny guy. But she just sighed. 'It was a joke,' she said quietly. 'What's wrong? Don't Judges ever tell jokes?' Getting in a quip but backing down, wishing she'd kept her mouth shut.

Haines watched her move across the room, slow but not the least bit self-conscious, the centre of attention and loving every second of it. She ever quoted stuff from a movie, you could bet your last cred it was one of hers. Then she was looking at him, giving him the smile, the come-on. This tough woman in a lousy motel room who still thought of herself as a star.

'Mr. Haines? Could you hand me a clean towel please?' she said, tossing back her hair, steam misting the mirror behind her.

He stared back, wanted to say to her, 'Honey, you're way pass the sell-by date,' but didn't have the guts. He gave her a polite smile instead and said, 'There's clean ones in the bedroom, ma'am. Why don't you get changed first, then come through and have something to eat?'

She shrugged and went into the bedroom and that was that. Hagenauer looking away as she closed the door behind her, turning back to his egg salad sandwich.

While they waited for Jean to finish dressing Haines told the rest of the team what Kurland had said, about the flash-forward, the premonition. Getting to the bit about feathers and blood when one of them butted in, Lockhart asking him why the hell he'd waited till now to tell them.

'It's been five minutes,' Haines said wearily. 'Lighten up, okay?'

Lockhart said excuse me but no, it wasn't okay, they should be getting the hell out of there **now**. Then Neff joining in saying you know, he's got a point, if our cover's blown we oughta do **something**. Lockhart beside him pulling his gun out his shoulder rig and checking the power-pack.

Haines was getting tired of this. 'Look, we're going to leave,' he said. 'Soon as Ms. Fremont is ready.' Looking over at Kurland now, seeing him sat in the corner, eating with his head down, keeping out of it.

'I don't know what we're doing here anyway,' Hagenauer said. 'Ask me, the broad should never a left Brit-Cit.'

'The broad is in protective custody,' Haines said. 'We're supposed to

keep her safe till this thing's over. You forget about that?'

He glanced at Kurland again, hoping he'd come in and help him out, but the guy was looking somewhere else. Sunglasses off, eyes narrowed, staring at the book shelf on the other side of the room, the candles on top of it...

'What's wrong?' Haines started to ask, then saw it for himself, the candle flames jittering, all of a sudden too bright. There was something in there. A speck of darkness in each of the flames, darting and bobbing, black pupils in yellow eyes.

Neff had seen it too. 'Oh Christ,' he said. Pulling his gun out of his shoulder holster and flicking off the safety. A Sechard .55, chrome and Teflon, what was known on the streets as a funtgun.

The pupils in the candles were dilating now, growing as they watched, as big as bird skulls and getting bigger. One of them burst suddenly, popping like a blister, and doused the candle with black ink. The flame sizzled out.

'Shoot it!' Lockhart shouted. 'Shoot the son of a bitch!'

He lifted his own gun and fired. Once, twice. Plaster flying from the wall, all the candles out now, putting one side of the room in darkness.

'What are we shooting at?' Haines asked, watching as the shadows bulked up in front of him. A shape in there now, rearing up, so much bigger than he'd thought it would be.

They were all firing now, Haines too, gun flashes lighting up the room like a strobe, making everything happen in slow motion. Watching as the bullets went right through the shapes and into the plasterboard walls. Then Hagenauer was screaming, head thrown back, blood in his mouth, and suddenly his arm was gone. Then his shoulder. Then half his ribcage. The thing in the darkness giggling and chattering as it took him apart.

Haines could see what was doing it now, some kind of animal, this one crouched in the light, three more back there in the shadows. They looked like apes in suits of armour, like they were built from some kid's model kit, but incomplete, half the pieces missing, gaps in the body you could see right through. Hunchbacked, with big hands that dragged on the floor and pointy Ku Klux Klan heads. Long cone-shaped heads that pivoted at the shoulders, angled downwards now so they pointed at the floor, knuckles of bone rolling around each cone like teeth on a drill-bit.

Then they were right there in front of him, those yellow buzzsaw teeth, the thing dipping its head towards Haines like a bird. He had time to squeeze off another shot before the pain hit, knocked him off his feet, and when he looked down there was a hole in his chest the size of a basketball. Wet and ragged, bone shining down there in the darkness where he didn't want to look.

He tried lifting his gun but it was slippery with blood and dropped from his fingers. Unconsciousness pressed down, made the room spin, and Haines wondered if what he was seeing now was real or imaginary, a man walking out of the mirror, stepping through it like a doorway. Small and skinny, looking like some carnival showman in bright green pants and a bright orange jacket, a white Venetian mask that covered the top half of his face.

Chigley. It had to be. Somehow he'd found the woman, sent those things here to clear the way, and now here he was in person, looking wild and stupid and scary all at the same time.

There was the sound of splintering wood and Haines turned his head to see one of the ape-things standing into bedroom, the door torn off at the hinges, a light on inside but the room empty. Curtains billowing out in front of the open window.

A breeze slipped in to the room, washing the smell of blood out of the air, giving Haines a moment of sudden clarity. He saw Chigley turn round, fury in his eyes now, knowing the woman had gone and telling his big ugly pets to go after her, to find the bitch and bring her back. Then the words were fading, the picture too, and Haines was carried off someplace deep and quiet and totally dark.

These last ten minutes, running down the Rue de Massy in a bathrobe and bare feet, passing parked cars and cliff-side houses but not a single person, Jean had managed to keep her mind empty. Get out of the

apartment, get as far away from Chigley as she could and hope those things would lose her. But now the thoughts were back, jangling in her head like loose change, and all of a sudden she knew she'd never make it.

She could hear them now, Chigley's pets, coming after her through the dark with their drill-bit heads and jigsaw bodies, whooping and cheering like some weird pageant. They were up in the aloe trees that ran alongside the road, a few hundred yards behind, she guessed, but getting closer.

Off to her left now she could see the harbour, dark water full of white shapes, yachts and pleasure vessels, and beyond that Monte-Carlo itself, a steep-sided hill with roads and buildings that climbed up in terraces. She was going downhill now, heading for the Casino in the centre of town, hoping she could lose herself amongst the lights and people.

Minutes later and she was on the main street, running past restaurants and brasseries, hotels with roofed-over foyers and doormen outside, getting looks from everyone but not letting it bother her one bit. The ape-things were too close. She could hear them further down the street, hollow thudding sounds as they leaped from car roof to car roof, people shouting and screaming as they passed by.

Jean turned left, then left again, heading down a narrow side-street that lead to the back of the Casino. It seemed like the best place to hide. Go in the back way and sneak upstairs, where the gaming rooms were filled with video cameras and floormen and armed security guards. She saw a light just up ahead, the car park attendant in his big yellow booth, and increased her pace. Then she was turning, running past the booth and the barriers and on into the underground parking lot. Voices shouting after her but her heartbeat drowning out the words. Her feet were raw and bloody but there was no way she was going to let up now, zig-zagging between cars and support pillars, knowing there was an elevator further on and heading straight for it.

She put on a burst of speed, side-stepped a green Daimler with tinted windows and what looked like oil pooling under the rear bumper, and ran straight into someone. A tall guy, heavy, big through the shoulders, built like a weight-lifter but looking more like a vicar in his dog collar and tunic, a red velvet smoking jacket with black beaverskin lapels, clothes that had gone out of fashion two hundred years ago.

Now she looked closer she saw there was blood on his mouth, all down his chin. She remembered the car leaking oil behind her and looked down to see that hey, surprise surprise, it wasn't oil after all. She knew that because there was a body down there too. A big guy soaked with blood, bite marks on his neck, face, shoulders. He'd been pretty good-looking too, judging by what was left.

She turned back to the figure in front of her, Mr Chigley and his pets forgotten now, part of another life, even though she could hear them gibbering somewhere back there in the darkness. Why did this guy, the vicar, look so familiar? She'd seen him before, she was sure of it. On TV maybe, or one of those glossy gossip pages in the Sunday supplements. Then he pulled a tortoiseshell cigarette holder out of his jacket pocket and she knew instantly who he was.

'I know you,' she said softly.

He smiled - the guy who looked like a vicar but wasn't - and said, 'My dear, I'd be most frightfully hurt if you didn't.'

Maybe her luck hadn't run out after all.

Five minutes later they were in the main gaming room and Jean had told Devlin everything. Eyes open, wetting her lips too much, telling him some wacko movie buff had fixated on her twenty-three years ago and had suddenly got tired of writing fan-mail. Devlin listened patiently, nodded in all the right places, and didn't believe a word of it.

People had noticed them by now, a big guy with blood down his shirt and a woman in a bright yellow bathrobe. Heads turning from the slot machines, a couple of security guards walking over with their hands on their gun belts, trying to look mean.

Devlin glanced back through the main doors. Chigley's pets were probably on their way up here right now, clambering up the elevator shaft like monkeys. Jean said she didn't know what they were, told him she'd never got a proper look at them, but Devlin had known straight away. Just the sound they made had been enough.

'Hey. You two. The hell you think you **doin'** here?'

Devlin turned and waited as the two security men came up to him, one tall and thin, the other short and round, the pair of them looking like a music hall double-act. It took them a second to recognise him but he knew it when they did. Eyes widening, the fat one taking a nervous step back, already starting to apologise.

'Gentlemen, I'd like to take you into my confidence, I really would, but I'm afraid that if I were to explain our current plight you'd both simply defecate on the spot.'

'Devlin.' Jean tugged at his arm, anxious to get out of here.

'Gee, I'm sorry 'bout that, Mr Waugh. For a minute there I didn't recognise you.' The fat security man squirming now, not sure what to do.

Devlin shrugged generously. 'There's absolutely no need to apologise.' He lowered his voice to a whisper. 'Actually, if you promise not to breathe a word of this to anyone, I shall let you into a little secret...'

The two guards exchanged looks.

'Ms. Fremont and I are fugitives.'

'Yeah?'

Devlin nodded. 'We're being quite mercilessly hounded by a pack of Lovemongers.'

The fat guard gave him a blank stare. '**Love**mongers?'

'A really quite wretched species. Demons from the Seventh Gulf. They're amateurs, of course, but shockingly enthusiastic.'

'**Demons?**'

Devlin sighed. 'Must you repeat simply everything I say? Yes. Demons.' Turning to Jean now. 'Isn't that right, my dear?'

She started to say something, got out a couple of words, then she was cut off by the sound of tearing metal, a thin sharp screech that set Devlin's teeth on edge; gave him an instant migraine. He was in time to see the elevator doors being ripped open, then the Lovemongers were bounding towards them, swinging through the entrance foyer on the backs of their hands. Four of them, gibbering like idiot children, dribbling tarry black saliva that hissed and sputtered when it hit the floor.

'Oh God.' Jean with one hand over her mouth, genuinely scared now, not even trying to act. Devlin took hold of her arm and pulled her quickly behind him, already wondering how he was going to play this. Cool and aloof, or fast and dirty, try to take them head-on.

People had seen the Lovemongers and were starting to panic, screams going off round the room like firecrackers, one after another. The security men were shouting now too, the thin one telling everyone it was okay, not to worry, while the fat one tried to get his gun out his holster. It was stuck in there, wedged tight, and he was still tugging at it when the first Lovemonger hit. A giant black fist went whistling past and the guy lost about thirty pounds instantly. Fat splashing across the wall like runny ice cream.

Things were speeding up now, everything happening at once. Jean backing away as the fat guard reached for her - blood on his hands - the thin one with his gun out letting off rounds. Devlin stepping sideways as two more Lovemongers came leapfrogging towards him, jumping across blackjack tables and roulette wheels as if they were on springs. Kicking up a spray of playing cards and poker chips.

The first one slammed straight into Devlin and knocked him clean off his feet. He waited as its head came dipping down, closer and closer, near enough to feel its breath on his face, then gave it a killing blow right to the chest. Both hands clasped to make one fist, a standard Kem-Kwong move. The Lovemonger screamed and lost its balance, thrashing and flailing like a kid throwing a tantrum, its hands and feet tearing chunks out floor.

Devlin twisted to one side as the other Lovemonger lashed out and missed him by an inch. He moved fast then, found an opening and suddenly had hold of its neck, a ball and socket joint that twisted and swivelled every

which way. He worked both thumbs in, digging down between bone and gristle, then pushed up hard. The Lovemonger let out a strangled shriek and its head popped clean off its shoulders, hit the floor and rolled around like a bloody traffic cone, still buzzing, those rows of teeth rattling like beads on an abacus.

Behind him, off to the right, there was a shout. High-pitched, the words going up and down, like someone reading a bunch of kids a bedtime story, putting on a funny voice:

'**Mr Chigley's coming to get you.**'

Devlin sneaked a glance at Jean and saw her shudder. Dark eyes in that white face, arms wrapped round her body like she was trying to keep warm. He heard her say, very softly, 'It's him.'

Back there in the darkness but coming closer, a man in a mask and a vaudeville suit, walking so slow and sure down the carpeted foyer he might have owned the place. Devlin tried to make out details - saw a kiss curl of dark hair, rings on fingers - but then the Lovemongers were back and the figure was blocked from view.

One of the Lovemongers padded forward and circled him slowly, like a tiger in a cage, trying to get his attention, and while his eyes were on it the other one leaped. Devlin saw the move coming and turned, swivelled on his left foot and kicked up with his right, hard. The blow hit right between the Lovemonger's legs, hefting it another foot into the air, and its pelvis shattered like rotten wood, pieces going everywhere.

He was about to take out the other one when a voice cut in, Chigley's womanly up-and-down tones calling the Lovemongers back, telling them to heel. They'll never move, Devlin thought. They're too fired up to even hear him. But a couple of seconds later the two surviving demons went trotting up to Chigley like well-trained dogs.

'Don't let him touch me,' Jean said behind him, her voice a whisper. 'Don't let him anywhere **near** me.'

Chigley heard. 'My dearest, darling Jean. I'd never harm you. You know that. I wouldn't harm a hair on your beautiful head.'

'I shan't pretend I even **begin** to understand what's going on here,' Devlin said calmly. 'But is this lady really that important to you?'

'Oh yes. She's everything to me.' Chigley stepping into the light now where Devlin could get a better look at him. 'I own her.'

'Really?'

Chigley nodded. 'Body and soul.'

Devlin sighed, wondering how things had ever gotten to be so complicated. He didn't even know why he was doing this. A woman bumps into him just before he can stash Rodovore's body and suddenly he's her guardian angel. Maybe it was the drink, he thought. Too much alcohol always made him aggressive, up-front, made him do things he'd regret later. And he knew he was going to regret this.

'You're not gonna **believe** him, are you?' Jean on her feet now, still scared but with that edge back in her voice. 'After what he's done?'

'I'm sure this is going to sound hideously feeble on my part,' said Devlin, 'but what exactly **has** he done?'

Jean glared at him but didn't say anything.

'I've given her fame and wealth,' Chigley said. '**That's** what I've done. Plucked her from the blighted streets of Brit-Cit and made her into a star.' He paused for effect. 'You might call me an impresario...'

Jean laughed. '**You?** Chigley, you're just a cheap shyster. A two-bit talent scout from Hell.'

'We made an agreement,' Chigley was saying now, turning back to Devlin, moving towards them with that slow cocksure walk of his. 'A pact. When I first met this young lady she was nobody. Oh, she had looks and ambition, of course, but very little else. I told her I could change all that. Promise me your soul, I said, and I'll give you everything you ever dreamed of. Twenty-three years in the fast lane.' Another pause. 'Needless to say, it was an offer she couldn't refuse.'

'Why only twenty-three years?' Devlin asked.

Chigley shrugged. 'It was the first number that came into my head.'

'You lousy son of a bitch.' Jean jumping in fast, spitting each word. 'Twenty-three years? You gotta be **kidding!**' Shouting now, rage transforming her, the light from the chandeliers making her wild and beautiful. 'It wasn't anywhere **near** that long. Three box office hits, a Best Supporting Actress award, and that was it. Finished. Kaput.' She turned to Devlin. 'You know what I did after **Oneshot?** Know where I worked then? On Swedish cable TV. You believe that? Rolling around a studio with three hermaphrodite dwarfs and a golden retriever!'

She was on a roll, looking like she had a whole lot more to say and wasn't going to stop till she'd said it, but Chigley did something then - a gesture with one hand - and she shut up abruptly. Devlin glanced round and saw that her mouth had gone, nothing there now but skin, pale and unbroken. Jean's eyes blazed, all those words locked up inside of her. Then she was scratching at the skin, digging in with her nails, bringing up blood and spittle, and Devlin had to stop her before she got down to bone.

Chigley gave him a sheepish grin. 'A deal's a deal.' Holding out his hands now; shrugging. 'What else can I do?'

Devlin thought about that one for a few seconds but nothing came to mind. He was drunk and tired and bored, with a migraine that set off fireworks in his head. Rodovore's body was still in the parking lot, rigor mortis setting in by now, and there wasn't long till sunrise. How much more time was he going to waste here?

'Just one final question, if I may?' Devlin asked, and when Chigley nodded he said, 'Who exactly **are** you?'

Jean moved then, throwing herself forward on those long slim legs, taking them all by surprise. She went for Chigley's throat. Murder in her eyes; hands out ready to strangle him. She covered half the distance before Chigley did anything, then the thin smile was back on his face as he lifted one hand, made that weird gesture again. There was a sound like birds taking off, a soft fluttering, and the playing cards scattered on the floor came suddenly to life. Shuffled by giant invisible hands, swooping down on Jean like fast-moving fish, flashes of red and black and white. They closed in around her, spinning in tight orbits, surrounding her like some weird kind of cage.

'You were saying?'

That was Chigley again, clearing his throat, trying to get the conversation back on course. He was anxious to finish this, too. Devlin could tell.

' Are you, by any chance, a demon yourself?'

There. Coming right out with it.

Chigley shook his head. 'No. But I am in touch with certain infernal forces. I have what you might call a hotline to Hell.' Chigley smiled as if it was a joke then moved over to Jean, transfixed in that blizzard of cards. 'Actually, if it's of any interest, before my fall from grace I was a priest myself.' He nodded. 'Just like you.'

Chigley raised one hand and there it was again, that gesture in empty air - like a royal wave or the twirl of a baton - and the Lovemongers blinked out of existence, leaving the smell of cooked meat behind them. Jean went next, fading slowly, her colour draining away to leave an outline, a stencil on the air, nothing. The playing cards rained to the floor, suddenly just playing cards again.

'Well,' said Chigley, 'thank heaven **that's** over with. It's back to the Gulfs for me.' He was fading out now too, erasing himself from the feet up - the bright green pants, the bright orange jacket, the mask - until there was just a hand left, one hand floating in thin air. A voice wavered up, sounding scratchy and far-away, a long-distance phone call. 'No hard feelings?'

Devlin took the hand in his and shook it firmly. 'Certainly not yet,' he said. Turning away as Chigley faded altogether, looking across the gaming room and out at the elevator, the doors buckled, ripped open, the empty shaft showing dark behind them. It looked like he was going to have to take the stairs.

He left through the emergency fire door, whistling cheerfully now, heading down to the parking lot with a spring in his step. Thinking of Rodovore - those blue eyes, that firm young body - and wondering if it wasn't about time he took up another hobby. Add another bow to his string.

Devlin Waugh, taxidermist.

Now **there** was a thought.

Breakdown on 9th STREET

PART 1

JUDGE DREDD

THIS IS **BUZZ BEEBERLY**, MEMBERSHIP NUMBER 003DASH-71MG2904STROKE01BEEB. WE'VE BROKEN DOWN ON 9TH STREET ABOUT HALF A KAY FROM THE INTERSECT. I'M PRETTY SURE IT'S THE DRIVE UNIT. SHE WON'T GO AT ALL.

DID YOU SAY **9TH STREET**, MR BEEBERLY?

BUZZ... THERE'S AN AWFUL LOT OF PEOPLE OUT THERE...

THAT'S 9TH STREET IN SECTOR 41?

YOU GOT IT! HOW LONG'LL YOU BE?

I'M SORRY... WE DON'T **MAKE** BREAKDOWN CALLS IN THAT AREA.

THIS **IS** THE MOPAD CLUB I'M TALKING TO? **HELLO...**?

MR BEEBERLY, DO EXACTLY AS I SAY. SECURE ALL DOORS AND WINDOWS IMMEDIATELY. FIND THE STRONGEST ROOM IN THE MOPAD AND BARRICADE YOURSELF IN. ARE YOU ALONE?

MY WIFE'S WITH ME.

STAY TOGETHER AT ALL TIMES. DO NOT ALLOW YOURSELVES TO BECOME SEPARATED.

SWEET GRUD! HOTLINE!

WE'RE INFORMING THE JUDGES OF YOUR SITUATION. KEEP YOUR FINGERS CROSSED. THERE'S JUST A CHANCE THEY MIGHT PULL YOU OUT IN TIME.

WH-WHAT'RE YOU TALKING ABOUT?

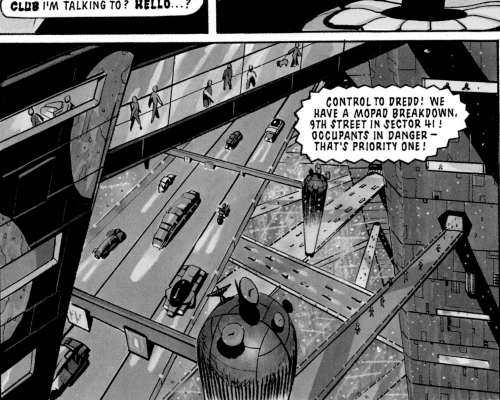

CONTROL TO DREDD! WE HAVE A MOPAD BREAKDOWN, 9TH STREET IN SECTOR 41! OCCUPANTS IN DANGER — THAT'S PRIORITY ONE!

I'M FOUR MINUTES AWAY AT LEAST! HAVEN'T YOU GOT ANYONE CLOSER?

THAT'S A NEGATIVE.

ON MY WAY!

WE'RE CUT OFF!

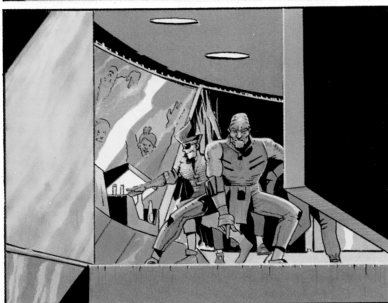

YOU EEN THERE, MAN? WE COMIN' TO GET YOU!

UPSTAIRS!

BADOW!

CRASHHH!

CONTROL, WE HAVE A SHOOTING, TUBLER SKED!

LOOKS LIKE A DOMESTIC. CAN'T IGNORE IT — REQUEST YOU REASSIGN THE 9TH STREET BREAKDOWN!

NOT POSSIBLE AT THIS TIME.

YOU DIRTY, TWO-TIMIN' PIECA —

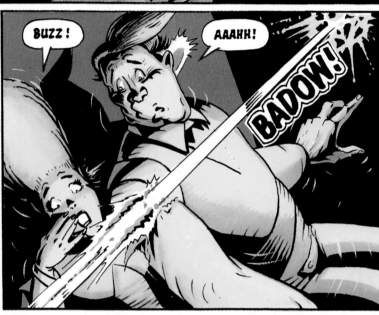

JUDGE DREDD

WHERE ARE THE JUDGES?

I'M SHORT-CUTTING THROUGH PROJECT BOULEVARD, CONTROL!

HONK! HONK!

DAMN JUDGES! THINK THEY **MAKE** THE LAW!

SKREEEEE

E.T.A. 9th STREET, TWO MINUTES!

COMIN' TA GET YA, FAT CATS!

OUR POOR MOPAD! WHAT'RE THEY **DOING** TO IT?

IT'S WHAT THEY'RE GOING TO DO TO **US**, BUZZ!

THAT'S RIGHT, SWEET CHIPS, YOU WORRY! HAHAHAHA!

THE SHOWER ROOM, HON! IT'S OUR ONLY CHANCE!

IT-IT'S NOT **DRAINING**, BUZZ!

THE TANK MUST BE FULL! I KNEW WE SHOULD'VE EMPTIED IT!

GOIN'S GOING

USE MY SHIRT — TRY TO BLOCK THE PIPE!

GONNA HAFTA LEAVE YOU, KIDS!

9TH

IT WON'T STAY IN!

PRESSURE'S TOO HIGH!

OH, BUZZ, WE COULD DROWN!

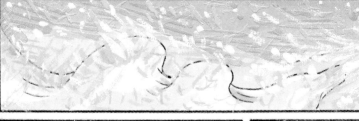

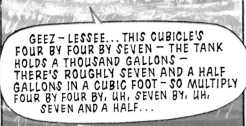

GEEZ — LESSEE... THIS CUBICLE'S FOUR BY FOUR BY SEVEN — THE TANK HOLDS A THOUSAND GALLONS — THERE'S ROUGHLY SEVEN AND A HALF GALLONS IN A CUBIC FOOT — SO MULTIPLY FOUR BY FOUR BY, UH, SEVEN BY, UH, SEVEN AND A HALF...

YES — YES — ?

I DUNNO, HON... I NEVER WAS MUCH GOOD AT MATHS...

OH, BUZZ!